Wholistic
Food Therapy

Sarah Thacker

Wholistic Food Therapy: A Mindful Approach to Making Peace with Food

ISBN-13: 978-0-9995899-0-8

ISBN-10: 0999589903

Printed in the United States of America

Wholistic Food Therapy

A Mindful Approach to Making Peace with Food

A Workbook and Expressive Journal

Sarah Thacker

Dedication

This book is dedicated to each person I have had the privilege of working alongside through your journey of making peace with food. You have taught me more than you could ever imagine. I am grateful to each of you, you are a constant inspiration.

Table of Contents

Introduction

Thank you for reading and choosing to use my book as a resource for making peace with food. I'd like to begin this journey by introducing myself and providing you with some information about my qualifications and my journey.

BACKGROUND
Sarah Thacker, LPC, ATR-BC, E-RYT-500, C-IAYT

I am a Licensed Professional Counselor in Virginia as well as a Registered and Board-Certified Art Therapist, Registered Yoga Instructor, Certified Yoga Therapist and Integrative Nutrition Health Coach. For nearly 10 years I worked in the mental health field helping clients through traditional art and talk therapy methods. While this was my passion, I began to feel disenchanted. I felt there was more I could offer to those in need. I was needing more. I was ready for a change.

Having a strong personal interest in nutrition, health, and wellness I chose to study at the Institute for Integrative Nutrition® (IIN). I had no idea where this training would lead me, but I knew I wanted to learn everything they had to offer.

After completing the health coach training I began advertising for individual health coaching separately from my work as a therapist, and I believed I was ready to take on both roles, respectively. However, I kept receiving requests from many people wanting aspects of both health coaching and therapy. Many of those who reached out wanted to address stress eating and emotional eating. One day I received a call from a prospective client inquiring if I was in fact a "food therapist". I laughed to myself, having this realization of what I had inadvertently become through my separate endeavors and that I could integrate them and become something like a "food therapist". I simply could not separate out health coaching from being a therapist.

Since then, I have directed my private practice outpatient work to using a more integrative approach to helping those who struggle with an emotional attachment to food. I offer opportunities to discover the origination of this attachment and to increase awareness around the amount of emotional distress this attachment creates.

This book is titled *Wholistic Food Therapy: A Mindful Approach to Making Peace with Food* as the intention is to integrate all aspects of healing; mind, body and spirit. No part is left out in this process. From what you eat and why you are eating it, to how your food choices make you feel physically and emotionally. To what you do with your time. To how you breathe, and how you think. While this is not a nutrition book specifically, I use the word *wholistic* as it implies addressing the *whole* person and the importance of eating *whole* foods at the same time.

Having a healthy relationship with food is possible. Although if you have struggled with this you know it is not an easy process. There are ups and downs along the way. There are setbacks as well as times of motivation and progress. Putting all of the pieces together is what this book hopes to help you do. Guiding you forward along your journey with specific tools for *wholistic* exploration to help you make peace with food.

How To Use This Book

This book offers a practical, creative and mindful experience that address-es food as well as a therapeutic approach to healing. You will learn to work through emotions, develop coping strategies and cravings protocols all with a focus on creative internal exploration throughout the process. Developing a healthy relationship with food takes time, effort, consistency and motivation. Taking time to put effort into the exercises in this book will be useful to help guide you along your path to healing. Ideally you want *food to be just food* while stress and emotions will have another distinct way to be addressed, felt and understood.

WHAT THIS BOOK IS
This book is intended to help guide you along your journey to making peace with food. This is a self-help style workbook and expressive journal. It may be of benefit to work through this book with a guide, a therapist, a health coach or an accountability partner.

As with many self-help books the tendency is to want to get through it to start feeling or living better. It is easy to get stuck in the fantasy of a quick fix or an immediate cure.

I recommend that you take it slowly. Use each chapter as a guide to help you focus, and work on the exercises every day in some way. Try to not move to the next chapter until you feel you have truly assimilated the in-formation and practices from the current chapter. Over time you will see progress. Take it one step at a time, one day at a time and you will begin to see your relationship with food evolve, shift and grow and in turn you will see your relationship with *yourself* grow and heal.

In order for change to be sustainable, it needs to be paced well and unhurried. Some of the more difficult elements of the process may take additional time and effort. There is no rush, let the path unfold one step at a time.

You can do this!

WHAT THIS BOOK IS NOT

This book does not promote any specific dietary theory or offer diet or nutrition advice. The purpose is to not become stuck in a dieting mentality. Diets to lose weight have an ending. Whereas a *wholistic* diet would be better framed as what you choose to eat, your way of life and your way of being with your food. The two are inherently different.

I do not want to tell you how to eat or give you a rigid plan. I want to help you become more trusting of your choices and encourage you listen to *YOUR* body. You are the expert on your body, how you feel, and how food makes you feel. I want to help you create your own personalized dietary theory, and a way of being with food that feels intuitive and instinctual and just right for *you*.

This book is *not* intended to be a substitute for therapy, or for those needing treatment for an eating disorder. If you are suffering with an eating disorder, please seek treatment as there is help available and hope for healing.

let the journey begin!

CHAPTER ONE

Preparing for Growth

CREATING A MINDFUL MINDSET

"We like to think of our champions and idols as superheroes who were born different from us. We don't like to think of them as relatively ordinary people who made themselves extraordinary."
–Carol Dweck

Preparing to move into this healthy positive direction of making peace with food, there will be some concepts woven throughout the book that will be helpful to understand prior to getting deep into the exploration.

The first is that there will be opportunities to create, to draw, and to express yourself artistically. If this sounds a little scary or even impossible to you, try not to throw it out just yet!

Popularized on the current market under the moniker of *Adult Coloring*, pre-drawn mandalas in adult coloring books have become widely used as a tool for relaxation. While this is therapeutic and very useful for relaxation purposes, the mandalas used in this book have a different intent and are blank. They are intended to be blank canvases ready for your expressive interpretations of your internal experience.

The mandalas in this book are intended to be containers and guides for your feelings. For your ability to witness your internal experience and the inner workings of your own mind.

The mandalas are not meant to be a masterpiece or overly analyzed. The mandalas you create through this process are a creative representation of the hard work you are committing to in this process of making peace with food as well as with yourself.

You are innately creative. Even if you say you cannot draw a straight line, that is okay. You do not have to draw a straight line. The purpose of using the art and creative process is to explore your internal world in a different way.

LEARNING NOT TO JUDGE YOUR *Creations* OR EXPECT A MASTERPIECE

An element that is important to use throughout this book is non-judgment. There are several opportunities to draw and write and creatively explore throughout this process. You do not need to be an art school graduate or a literary guru. These exercises are for everyone. Try not to judge what your drawings look like. They are not meant to be critiqued in that way. The drawings are all about the process of creating and allowing a deeper exploration into your true self.

The majority of the drawings are mandalas. Mandala means circle or healing circle in the ancient language of Sanskrit. It is a place of holding, a place to let your emotions and internal experiences rest. The circle is meant to be a guide not a barrier. Meaning, you do not need to stay inside the lines!

These drawings and journaling opportunities are intended to illuminate your process. Try not to overthink it. Have fun. Allow yourself to explore through line, shape, color, form and words.

For the drawing exercises, any material will do. You might like oil pastels, colored pencils, and markers. Use what feels good for you or whatever is available; even crayons! This is your book, let it be a safe place for exploration, creative inspiration and expression.

USING *Mindfulness* AND *Visualization* THROUGHOUT THE PROCESS

The mindfulness exercises are designed to enhance your inner exploration and process.

Mindfulness is being present from moment to moment without judgment of your experience. It allows you to be an active participant in your life. To be truly awake and present; active in the unfolding of your life's path.

Visualization is projecting yourself into the possibilities you can create within your mind. The ability to imagine what you want within your mind's eye. To see, to rehearse, to practice mentally. Visualization prepares you mentally for what you want to create within your life.

Using mindfulness and visualization exercises help to put what you want into your mindset while clearing out the unnecessary space of mental distractions. Mental clutter can include excuses, negative self-talk, and judgmental thoughts.

The intention is to move away from the distractions and potential negativity of the mind and move into the present moment. Eating mindfully is a significant component of this process and mindfulness techniques help to free up mental space in order to be present with your food, with every moment and with your life.

PREPARING YOUR *Mindset*

Your mindset is responsible for the majority of what you get done. When you put your mind to something, typically it means you are going to make it happen. Having the mindset and determination to push through blocks that have been set by fear, limiting beliefs and negative self-talk will be a challenging, but a necessary part of this process.

Everyone has limiting beliefs, and when you get stuck in them, often you move into a mindless space and feel complacent, unmotivated and stuck. This book will help to guide you through these challenges, however, you will have to do the at times uncomfortable work to get there. You will have to believe in yourself. You will have to believe in your capacity for growth and change.

LEARNING TO FOLLOW YOUR *Breath*

Breathing is an automatic process. You will breathe whether you are thinking about it or not. By becoming aware of your breath and taking control of it, you can change your breathing patterns and change your perception on your everyday life. Breathing is the most powerful method of reducing stress and maintaining balance physically, mentally and emotionally. It is important when using the exercises in this book that you are breathing fully and deeply. The following exercise allows you to learn to breathe deeply and completely.

Diaphragmatic Breathing

Begin by placing one hand on your abdomen and one on your chest. Notice which hand is moving as you inhale and which hand is moving as you exhale. Breathe in through your nose and out through your nose.

Now begin to direct your breath to expand your abdomen deeply into your hand as you inhale, and draw your navel back towards your spine as you exhale. Allow the hand on the chest to remain as still as possible.

Breathing in this manner assures that you are aligning yourself with parasympathetic nervous system engagement: rest and digest mode. When your body is in a state of true rest, it will be able to focus on digestion, one the biggest and most energetic jobs your body has each day. When in a state of sympathetic nervous system arousal, there is additional adrenaline and cortisol in your system which puts your body into a state of fight, flight or freeze.

Breathing deeply can help to move your nervous system from the sympathetic response: fight, flight or freeze to parasympathetic nervous system response: rest and digest.

Rest and digest: This is where you want to live. This is how you want to breathe.

Understanding how to breathe will impact how you feel in your daily life. Breathing is incorporated into many of the exercises throughout this book and is a valuable tool to become more mindfully present in every moment. The breath is free. It is *always* available to offer a place of serenity and calm.

CHAPTER TWO

Creating Your Foundation

DEVELOPING YOUR VISION

"Your vision will become clear only when you can look into your own heart. Who looks outside, dreams; who looks inside, awakens." -Carl Jung

This *wholistic* process begins with creating your vision for what you want to accomplish in your life. For any structure to be stable it must have a solid foundation. Your vision coupled with your goals, guide you along your way to fully living your vision. Having this solid foundation of knowing what you want and then preparing yourself through goal setting to achieve what you want is vital.

I encourage you to take your time with this chapter. Getting a clear understanding and grasp on your vision and your goals will allow you to have a plan for moving forward. Establishing a solid foundation here will help tremendously as you move forward on your path of making peace with food.

This *wholistic* process is meant to be traveled one step at time with focus and determination, patience and integration. Try to let go of any thoughts or hopes of perfection. Perfection simply does not exist. If you are holding onto an expectation of perfection, in this moment, let it go.

Throughout this workbook and expressive journal there are opportunities to reflect, to feel, and to think. Take your time with them and allow your process to unfold.

It all begins with creating your vision. Once you have it, it will be helpful to regularly ask yourself: **Does this choice support my vision?**

There are often mental and emotional struggles in working towards your vision. This is part of the process and what this book is all about. Having questions to ask yourself such as the one above and reminders of what you want will help you maintain your focus.

Creating Your Vision

Think about what you want in your life. What will allow you to live a life that you love? What is your vision for your life? What do you need to live a life where you feel engaged and active in achieving what you want? You can begin with bullet points or create an outline, or if you prefer, just free write. This is the first step in creating a roadmap to getting to where you want to go. This can be a challenging exercise. Take your time with it. Be present with yourself as you ponder, visualize and allow yourself to believe in the possibility that what you want is attainable and on its way.

Your vision:

_____

_____

_____

_____

_____

_____

_____

_____

_____

_____

_____

_____

_____

_____

_____

_____

_____

_____

_____

_____

_____

_____

Read through your vision. Now consider your vision in relation to food and making peace with food. Take some time to ponder how your life might be different when your relationship with food is in a healthy space.

Imagine the possibility of what you can visualize and allow yourself to align with the belief that you *will* have a healthy relationship with food.

How will it change you to have a healthy relationship with food?

_____

_____

How will it impact your relationships to have a healthy relationship with food?

_____

_____

_____

How will it impact how you feel about yourself to have a healthy relation-ship with food?

_____

_____

_____

Reflect on what you have written about this possibility. Does this change your overall vision? If so, how?

_____

_____

Mindful Visualization

MINDFUL MOMENT: Set a timer for 5 minutes and allow yourself to believe in this possibility of having a healthy relationship with food. Believe in the impact it will have on your life. For 5 minutes visualize yourself with a healthy relationship with food and the effect on your life. Reflect on this experience here:

What came up for you in this time?

_____

_____

What fears were present?

_____

_____

What positive thoughts did you have?

_____

_____

What will it take to believe in the possibility of making peace with food?

_____

_____

Creating Your Vision Board

"Create the highest, grandest vision possible for your life, because you become what you believe."
-Oprah Winfrey

Taking time to create a visual representation of your vision offers a creative way to energize your vision as well as an opportunity for growth and change and deeper internal reflection.

Materials:
A collection of images
Poster board or piece of card board-about 11x14 to 18x24
Scissors
Glue

Process:
Begin collecting images that you are attracted to for any reason. Whether you are inspired by them, interested in them, find them beautiful, or the image resonates with you in any other way. You can collect words, quotes, and letters as well as images. Collect from any resources available. Magazines are often the most accessible, but you can additionally look through old books or photographs or anywhere else you may find images relating to your vision. Keep the images in a safe place, like a folder or box. After you have a large number of images and are ready to create your board, designate a specific time to give to the process. Plan for about 2-3 hours.

Set your intention to create a vision board of what you would like to manifest into your life. Reflect on your vision and the possibility of making peace with food. Look through your images and pull the ones that match your intention for any reason. After you have sorted through the images, begin trimming them if needed and pasting them to your board. Try not to overthink this. Go with your intuition and imagination.

Reflection:
Once your vision board is complete, spend time reflecting on your board. Journal about your vision board and share it with someone. Sharing your vision, and seeing it reflected back to you through someone else's words of encouragement is a positive experience. Sharing your vision helps it to become a reality. Having excitement for your vision may be contagious and you may inspire someone to create their vision as well!

Now that you have your vision, and you are able to consider the possibility of having a healthy relationship with food, it is time to set your goals.

Goals help to define what you want and how to get there. They are the action focus of your vision and allow your vision to come to life.

The goal is the specific overview, while the action steps are the incremental steps to help you get to where you want to go.

With your vision firmly set as a possibility-something you can visualize as a reality-what goals stand out for you in relation to making peace with food?

Are your goals self-care oriented with a focus on health and wellness topics such as: exercising, eating more vegetables, drinking more water, starting to work with a health coach, meditating, getting massages, taking dance or yoga classes?

Are your goals about creating more balance in your life such as: finding a new less stressful job, working through problems in your relationship, or finding your passion?

While the focus of your vision may be on making peace with food, the goals do not necessarily have to be all about food and lifestyle. The reason food may have become the coping skill for stress and difficult emotions may be due to other life stressors that need to be addressed.

Whatever your goals may be, and you may have many goals that lead you toward your vision, begin to clarify them here.

Here is an example:

Goal 1: *To add 2 nutrient dense foods into my daily diet.*

Action Step 1: Develop a list of nutrient dense foods that I like to eat.

Action Step 2: Look up recipes that use these nutrient dense foods.

Action Step 3: Keep a log of the foods I have added and the recipes I enjoy.

Action Step 4: Reflect on the foods I have added daily to ensure I am reaching my goal.

Action Step 5: Re-evaluate in one month and consider increasing to 3 nutrient dense foods daily.

Now it's your Turn!

Developing Your Goals

GOAL 1: _____

Action Step 1: _____

Action Step 2: _____

Action Step 3: _____

Action Step 4: _____

Action Step 5: _____

Goal Reflection: Why is this goal important to you?

_____

_____

What will it mean to you to achieve this goal?

_____

_____

Who will support you in achieving this goal?

_____

How will you feel when you achieve this goal?

_____

How will you know when it is truly integrated?

_____

GOAL 2: _____

Action Step 1: _____

Action Step 2: _____

Action Step 3: _____

Action Step 4: _____

Action Step 5: _____

Goal Reflection: Why is this goal important to you?

_____

_____

What will it mean to you to achieve this goal?

_____

_____

Who will support you in achieving this goal?

_____

_____

How will you feel when you achieve this goal?

_____

_____

How will you know when it is truly integrated?

_____

_____

GOAL 3: _____

Action Step 1: _____

Action Step 2: _____

Action Step 3: _____

Action Step 4: _____

Action Step 5: _____

Goal Reflection: Why is this goal important to you?

_____

_____

What will it mean to you to achieve this goal?

_____

_____

Who will support you in achieving this goal?

_____

_____

How will you feel when you achieve this goal?

_____

_____

How will you know when it is truly integrated?

_____

_____

Once you have your goals it is essential to stay on top of their implementation. Write how you will commit yourself to pursuing your goals and manifesting your vision:

How will you stay focused on your goals?

_____

_____

_____

How will you plan which action steps to choose from day to day?

_____

_____

_____

How will you maintain your motivation to use your action steps and stay focused?

_____

_____

_____

Who will you share your goals with for encouragement and support? What will that be like for you?

_____

_____

_____

Intention

"When you set an intention, when you commit, the entire universe conspires to make it happen."
-Sandy Forster

Your ability to believe in the possibility of making peace with food begins to shift your mindset from worry and frustration to hope and positivity. Having your vision and your goals to guide you will help to make this possible.

Setting a daily intention will help to maintain your belief in what you are capable of achieving. It will allow you to believe in what you can do for yourself, and how you can keep your vision at the forefront of your mind and the driver of your life.

One of the most valuable exercises you can do is to set your daily intention. Your intention, coupled with commitment and dedication, create the ability to follow through with what you want. When you set your intention, you set a powerful force in action for growth and change.

Where you place your attention, your energy will follow. Imagine putting your attention on what you want and allowing your energy to flow into that space. If you set your intention and allow your energy to follow, change will happen, it will have to.

Are you ready?

Setting Your Daily Intention

Setting your daily intention is about what you want to accomplish. What you want to bring to your day. What your hopes are. Set your intentions for your day each morning. Spend time writing them down, visualizing and even stating your intentions out loud.

Your intentions may change from day to day. They might include your action steps from your goals or just how you want to be with yourself throughout the day.

Here are some examples:

-My intention is to practice patience today.
-My intention is to read for one hour today.
-My intention is to make each choice with the mindset that I will manifest my vision.
-My intention is to spend 5 minutes deep breathing today.

Choose your intention based on what feels right to you each day.

Over the next week, practice setting your daily intentions, and then reflect on them at the end of the day in the following chart:

Date	Daily Intention	Evening Reflection on Intention and Impact on Your Day
Example: Day 1: 9/12/17	My intention is to spend 5 minutes deep breathing today.	Today I lived my intention and feel more relaxed as a result.
Day 1:		
Day 2:		
Day 3:		
Day 4:		
Day 5:		
Day 6:		
Day 7:		

What was it like for you to set your daily intentions?

_____

_____

_____

Were you able to stay focused on your intentions throughout your day?

_____

_____

_____

Did anything surprise you when you reflected on your intentions at the end of the day?

_____

_____

_____

How will you use this practice going forward?

_____

_____

_____

Stay True to your _vision_ and personal _intentions_ and you will see the power of your vision come to _life!_

CHAPTER THREE

Healthy Foundations

SETTING UP THE BASICS WITH WHOLE FOODS FOR NUTRITIONAL HEALING

"The doctor of the future will no longer treat the human frame with drugs, but rather will cure and prevent disease with nutrition." -Thomas Edison

This book is not so much about food and nutrition as it is about healing your relationship with food. However, as you make peace with food, it will be useful to address certain trigger foods while increasing foods that are nutrient dense. This is not meant to be nutrition advice. This is about developing awareness of the impact of what you eat has on you mentally, emotionally, physically, spiritually and energetically.

This chapter addresses nutrition from a standpoint of ensuring that you are setting up the basics with food. You will be adding in healthy foods that allow you to thrive and feel your best. You will focus on foods that are nourishing and help create a sense of greater health and well-being.

Imagine that there is no one specific dietary theory that is best to follow all throughout your life. Imagine that you are the expert on your body. You know what your body needs. You know best how to feed yourself in a way that allows you to feel energized and healthy. Can you imagine this possibility? While this might sound ideal, unfortunately, this is often not the case. You may not trust yourself with food. You may not connect with your intuition around food.

Throughout this process you are encouraged to pay attention to *how food makes you feel* on all levels. Your focus is how it impacts your energy, your mood as well as your physical body. This creates self-awareness and empowerment to feel confident about your choices.

While there are so many dietary theories and so many are contradictory to each other, there is an overlap that most seem to agree on:

The more your food is in its whole form, the healthier it is to consume.

In this process of making peace with food, let's start with what we do know. Until you feel comfortable with the absolute basics, there is no need to change anything else. Always remember to focus on the basics.

Basic #1: GREENS

Eating whole foods is ideal, and eating your veggies is a very good thing. Especially when the veggie is a dark leafy green vegetable. The more you take in foods that are whole and healthy, typically the better you will feel.

For the next week, challenge yourself to eat one serving of leafy greens every day. That's it. No other changes in your food are necessary. Integrate the greens and pay attention to your body's reaction. That is the challenge.

While you are making this healthy change, keep a log of your intake of greens, along with notes about digestion, mood, and energy. If you are accustomed to keeping a calorie focused food log, try to let that go, or at least keep it separate. The focus of the log here is to help you focus on what is going well, adding in a leafy green, and its impact on you. That is all. The log gives you immediate feedback about how this change will affect you in several areas.

Some examples of leafy green vegetables include: broccoli, kale, spinach, collards, chard, mustard and dandelion greens, arugula, romaine, cabbage and Brussels sprouts. The list can continue!

Some of the best ways to get in leafy greens and a range of healthy nutrition is following the four S's of cooking: **S**oup, **S**alad, **S**tir fry, and **S**moothies (there are some recipes coming later in this chapter). Have fun with it, get creative and go green!

Basic # 2: WATER

Drinking water is essential to health. Try to drink plain, filtered water and see if after one week you can get used to this. Many people are accustomed to having a lot of flavor in their drink choices. This commonly causes them to be enticed back to sodas or other sugary beverages. So initially drinking just plain water can be, well, kind of plain. Just give it a go and see the impact.

If you struggle with plain water, try a product like an *Aquazinger*, or another infusing method. You can put ginger, fresh herbs like mint or basil, citruses such as lemon or orange, fresh cucumber or strawberries in the base and then fill with water and the strainer allows the flavor to seep through but no pulp. Leaving you with tasty flavored water with no added sugars or artificial flavors!

EXERCISE ONE
Log Your Greens and Water

For the next week challenge yourself to eat one leafy green per day and attempt to get 8 or more glasses of water per day. Keep a log of how it impacts you here in the following chart:

Day	Green	Water Amount
Example: Day 1:	1 Cup Roasted Broccoli	8 Glasses
Day 1:		
Day 2:		
Day 3:		
Day 4:		
Day 5:		
Day 6:		
Day 7:		

Digestion	Mood	Energy
Normal	Positive, felt happy much of the day	Normal with a lull in the afternoon

After completing the week-long Greens and Water challenge reflect on your experience here:

What changes did you notice in your digestion?

_____

_____

_____

_____

What changes did you notice in your mood?

_____

_____

_____

_____

What changes did you notice in your energy?

_____

_____

_____

_____

What surprised you the most?

_____

_____

_____

Did this week-long challenge impact your food choices in other ways? If so, how?

_____

_____

_____

Did this week-long challenge have an impact on your self-esteem? If so, how?

_____

_____

_____

As you complete this week-long challenge of incorporating eating leafy greens and drinking a good amount of water into your daily routine it will hopefully become a habit. Keep going with it. This is an element that never ends and creates the foundation for better overall health, wellness, and a healthy relationship with food.

While the focus has been on leafy greens so far, it is important to get a wide range of colorful vegetables into your meals. The average person eating a Standard American Diet (also known as the SAD diet) takes in very few servings of vegetables per day. Aim for more than what you are currently consuming. The more vegetables in their whole, fresh form the better!

EAT A *Rainbow* OF COLOR

Here is a short of list of examples to eat a wide variety of colorful fruits and vegetables:

Red: tomatoes, apples, beets, raspberries, strawberries, watermelon, radishes, red peppers, red onion, red cabbage, red chard

Orange: Oranges, orange peppers, carrots, sweet potatoes, yams, apricots, peaches

Yellow: Bananas, golden beets, yellow carrots, potatoes, yellow peppers, pineapple

Green: All dark leafy greens and salad greens, asparagus, avocados, cucumbers, celery, broccoli, green beans, sprouts

Blue: Blueberries, currants

Purple: Grapes, blackberries, purple cabbage, purple potatoes, eggplant, beets, plums

Gain inspiration from this list and see where you can increase the rainbow of colors in your grocery cart.

Nutrient DENSITY

When eating a more *wholistic* diet, incorporating nutrient dense foods is essential. Nutrients include: *fiber, carbohydrates, fat, vitamins, minerals, and protein.* When you hear the word "superfood" it indicates that the food contains many if not all of these nutrients, and is considered nutrient dense. Here are some options that will help to increase your nutrient density by incorporating more nutrient dense foods into your daily diet:

Fiber: any plant based foods such as: vegetables, fruits, whole grains, nuts, seeds, beans

Carbohydrates: any plant based foods such as: vegetables, fruits, whole grains, nuts, seeds

Fat: fatty fish such as wild-caught salmon and sardines, meat- ideally grass-fed beef and free-range chicken, whole eggs, nuts, seeds, avocados, dark chocolate, dairy, olive oil, coconut oil

Vitamins and minerals: any plant based foods such as: vegetables, fruits, whole grains, nuts, seeds, as well as fatty fish, grass-fed beef, dairy, eggs, beans, most foods in their *whole* form

Protein: All meat, fish, seafood, dairy, eggs, beans, nuts, legumes

Another element that is important and will be covered more in depth later in the book is taste as a nutrient. It is important that you enjoy what you are eating to create a sense of satisfaction and true satiety from your food.

THE FOUR S's OF *Cooking*

As mentioned above, when adding in more healthy nutrients, going by the four **S**'s of cooking can be helpful. Using these colorful vegetables and fruits and nutrient dense foods, begin to incorporate more nutrients into your daily diet.

Following is a recipe from each category: **S**oup, **S**alad, **S**tir fry and **S**moothies. This is where you can get creative. Use these recipes as guidelines. Find vegetables you love and get cooking! For more healthy recipes visit my website: www.wholisticfoodtherapy.com.

Get inspired and get cooking!

Soup

CREAMY SWEET POTATO AND GREEN GARLIC SOUP

Ingredients:

1 large onion, chopped
8 cloves of garlic, chopped
3-5 cups of vegetable or other stock
1 large bunch of kale, roughly chopped
1 large bunch of Swiss chard, roughly chopped
1 large bunch of fresh spinach
1-2 tablespoons of fresh sage, chopped
2 large sweet potatoes, skin left on, cut into 1-inch cubes
1 cup of cashews, soaked overnight (optional)
salt and pepper, to taste
green apple and dulse flakes optional

Directions:

Cook the onion on medium in a large pot with a little avocado or coconut oil and a splash of stock for about 5-7 minutes.

Add the sweet potato and 1-2 cups of the stock, cook for 7-10 minutes or until the sweet potatoes are just becoming soft.

Add the kale, chard and garlic and just enough stock to cover, cook for 15 minutes.

Add the sage cook for 10 minutes.

Make the cashew cream- blend the soaked and drained cashews with just enough water to almost cover the cashews, blend on high for about 30 seconds or until smooth and creamy. Forget to soak the cashews? No need to fret. Put one rounded cup of cashews in the blender with 1 cup of broth, blend until smooth.

Mix the cashew cream into the soup.

Using small batches blend the soup in the blender adding a large handful of fresh spinach to each batch, blend until smooth.

Serving suggestions: serve with a finely diced tart green apple (about 2 slices per serving) and dulse flakes sprinkled on top.

Salad

QUINOA SALAD WITH A CREAMY SAGE DRESSING

Ingredients:

1 cup quinoa
1 1/2 cups green lentils
2 medium sweet potatoes, peeled and diced
1 shallot or 3 green onions
1 teaspoon of dried sage
Juice of 1/2 a lime
1 tablespoon olive oil
salt and pepper, to taste
Big bunch fresh arugula

For the Creamy Sage Dressing:

1 cup cashews (if you are nut free, you can add additional oil and leave these out)
1/2 cup water
2 tablespoons fresh sage
1 large clove garlic or 2 small cloves
2 teaspoons brown rice miso paste

Directions:

Preheat oven to 400°F. Toss diced sweet potatoes in olive oil, dried sage, and salt and pepper to taste, place on a roasting pan and roast for 20-30 minutes or until soft on inside and crispy on the outside, turning them once during cooking.

Cook quinoa (add 1 cup quinoa to 2 cups water, bring to a boil, once boiling reduce heat to low and simmer for 15 minutes). Cook lentils (bring 2 1/2 cups water to a boil, add lentils, reduce heat to low and simmer for 30 minutes).

Lightly sauté garlic and fresh sage in a spritz of olive oil for about 5 minutes. Place cashews, water, sage, garlic and miso into a blender and blend until smooth and creamy, add water if needed to achieve desired consistency. Use the sauté pan to lightly sauté shallot or green onions for about 5-8 minutes, stir in lime juice and shallot to cooked quinoa.

To serve, place quinoa at the bottom of the bowl, add lentils, sweet potatoes, fresh arugula and top with dressing.

Bonus SALAD RECIPE

SUPER SALAD

Ingredients:

1 large bunch of greens of your preference (romaine, spinach, chard, kale, combination...)
1-2 cups veggies of your choice, diced or chopped
1/2 cup fruit of your choice, chopped if needed (apple, pear, any berry, melon...)
Optional: 1/2 cup nut or seed of your choice (walnuts, almonds, pecans, sunflower seeds, pumpkin seeds...)
Optional: 1/4 cup cheese of your choice (parmesan, goat cheese, manchego, cheddar)
Dressing of your choice or a drizzle of olive oil and vinegar

Preparation: Put all in a large bowl and enjoy! You will have plenty to share!

 **FRY**

RAINBOW VEGGIE STIR FRY

Ingredients:

2 cups chopped vegetables of your choosing—try to get in a rainbow of color here (e.g. kale, bok choy, asparagus, red yellow and green peppers, onion, carrots, mushrooms, etc.)
1 tablespoon fresh ginger root, finely chopped or shredded (peel first)
3 cloves fresh garlic, finely chopped
3 tablespoons avocado or sesame oil
1 tablespoon brown rice vinegar
3 tablespoons coconut aminos or no wheat tamari sauce
2 cups chopped protein of your choice: cooked tofu, beef or chicken
2 cups brown rice, cooked

Directions:

Heat a medium sauté pan or wok to medium, add oil and stir in vegetables. Cook for 5-8 minutes on medium-high stirring in garlic and ginger throughout the several minutes, then lower heat to medium-low and add coconut aminos or tamari and cooked protein of your choice, stir together for 2 minutes. Lower heat to low for 5 minutes stirring occasionally.

Serve over brown rice and enjoy!

Smoothie

CHOCOLATE STRAWBERRY SMOOTHIE

Ingredients: (serves 2)

2 cups plain unsweetened almond or coconut milk
1 tablespoon cacao (raw powdered chocolate)
¾-1 cup frozen strawberries
1-2 cups loosely packed spinach (or other greens)
1/2 cup peanuts or almonds (optional)
1-2 dates (or 1 small apple or 1 banana)
1 tablespoon ground flax seed
1 tablespoon preferred protein powder

Directions:

Blend ingredients together on medium high to high until desired consistency, adding water or additional non-dairy milk as necessary.

Use these recipes as guides and get creative adding more vegetables into your meals. If these recipes do not suit you, keep searching. There are healthy greens and veggies out there for everyone!

As you add more colorful vegetables, fruits and nutrient dense foods into your diet, notice the impact on how you feel on all levels. Reflect here:

_____

_____

_____

_____

_____

CHAPTER FOUR

Managing Your Stress
BRIDGING THE GAP BETWEEN FOOD AND STRESS EATING

"Tension is who you think you should be, relaxation is who you are." -Chinese Proverb

Many can relate to being a "stress eater." There was most likely a time in your life when your stress was eased and soothed by the comfort of food. This release of stress with food may have formed as a coping strategy and expanded into the multitude of emotions entangled with stress. This food-mood connection is very satisfying, very strong, and can become very damaging.

Ideally, food is just food, where the focus is on nourishment, taste, and the pleasure of eating. You do not want food to be a coping strategy for stress, or any emotion.

Stress is thought to be responsible for many diseases and illnesses not only because of how the stress response impacts the physical body, but also because of the lifestyle habits that it impacts. Often stress negatively impacts areas that contribute to good health such as sleep, nutrition, freshly prepared meals and time for self-care.

This *Circle of Life* is a helpful exercise to observe the balance in your life, offering a visual representation of what is in balance and what is out of balance. The more out of balance life becomes the more stress you are likely experiencing in your life.

Circle of Life

Complete the *Circle of Life* exercise. It creates a visual representation of the current balance in your life. Usually when life is out of balance it creates a challenge for food and wellness to be in balance. The exercise considers primary foods to be the elements in your life that nourish you and secondary food to be the food you actually eat. When your primary foods are out of balance it directly impacts your secondary food.

INSTRUCTIONS:

Look at each section and place a dot on the line based on how satisfied you are with each area of your life. A dot placed at the center of the circle would indicate dissatisfaction, while a dot placed closer to the edge indicates complete satisfaction. Once you have placed your dot on each of the lines, connect the dots to see your circle of life. You will have a clear visual representation of any imbalances so you can determine where you could benefit from spending more time and energy to create balance and joy in your life.

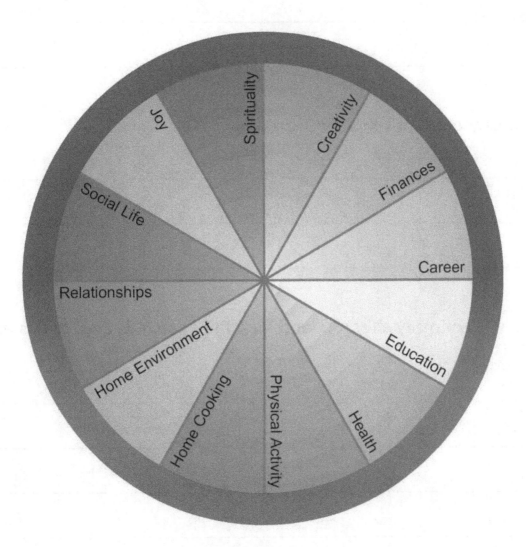

© 2011 Integrative Nutrition Inc.

When reflecting on your *Circle of Life*, what stands out to you the most?

_____

_____

_____

Are there any elements that surprise you?

_____

_____

_____

Describe your primary stressors and how they are reflected in this exercise:

_____

_____

_____

_____

_____

_____

Mandala

REPRESENTING YOUR STRESS

On the next page, there is a circle, ready for you to create. This is a mandala, a place to hold your feelings, your thoughts, your internal experiences ready to be expressed.

Begin by selecting a color that represents how you are feeling after reflecting on your primary stressors. Notice how you experience your feelings in your body and stay present with them.

Use the mandala (circle) as a guide, not a barrier. This is a place to use creative expression to explore and express your feelings through art making.

Use lines, shapes, colors, and forms to express how you feel about the stress in your life. You can change colors throughout, just begin with one that best represents how you feel when you think about your stress.

Try not to judge your experience. Just create. This requires getting out of your head, not thinking about it, but allowing yourself to generate a visual representation of what your stress looks like and offering a space to release it.

Reflect on your mandala.

Put words to your creation and write the title here:

_____

How does your mandala make you feel?

_____

_____

_____

What stands out to you the most?

_____

_____

_____

What can you learn from this mandala?

_____

_____

_____

Now that you have created a mandala that represents the stress in your life, you will have an opportunity to create one following a mindful moment.

Mandala

REFLECTING ON LETTING GO

MINDFUL MOMENT: Take a moment to soften your gaze toward the ground or close your eyes. Bring your attention to the rhythm of your breath. Allow it to become steady, deep and even. Expand your abdomen with each inhale, draw your navel towards your spine with each exhale.

Set a timer for 5 minutes. Breathing in through the nose, and out through the nose. Begin to use the mantra: *"Let go."* Saying *let* as you inhale and *go* as you exhale. Imagine bringing in serene and relaxing energy as you inhale and all the stress in your life releasing with each exhale. Return your focus to your breath and the mantra *"Let go"* when your mind wanders.

On the next page, create a mandala that reflects how you feel following this mindful moment. This opportunity to create mental calm and releasing of stress. Begin by selecting a color that represents how you are feeling. You can change colors throughout. Just begin with one that best represents how you feel. Try not to judge your experience. Just create.

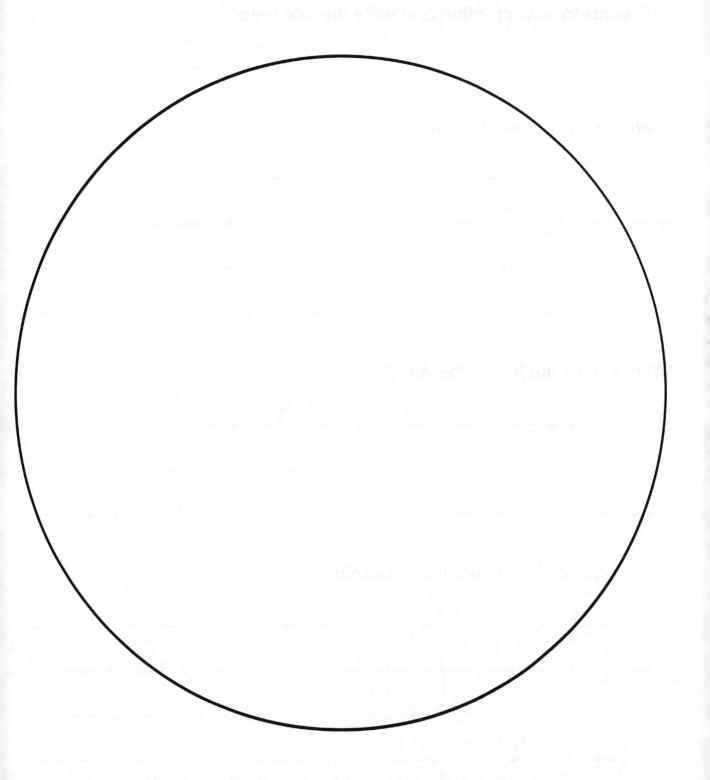

Reflect on your mandala.

Put words to your creation and write the title here:

_____

How does your mandala make you feel?

_____

_____

_____

_____

What stands out to you the most?

_____

_____

_____

What can you learn from this mandala?

_____

_____

_____

_____

Consider the two mandalas, how are they different?

_____

_____

_____

_____

_____

Look at the two mandalas. Notice through your expressive creation the impact that your stress has on you mentally, emotionally and physically. Notice through your expressive creation the impact that a calming mindful practice has on you mentally, emotionally and physically.

Now that you can see the difference, how will you take your life back from stress?

_____

_____

_____

_____

_____

_____

_____

COPING WITH *Stress*

Having coping skills, regular self-care and a plan can help you incorporate more health and wellness practices, reduce your stress while moving in the direction of making peace with food. The problem often lies in, if you have been using food to soothe emotional distress for a long time, what will you do instead? This exercise is designed to help develop alternative options to food when faced with stress.

Some examples of coping skills include:

Calling a friend, reading, breathing, laughing, meditating, stretching, exercising, taking a walk, doing yoga, gardening, learning something new, starting a new hobby, getting a massage, cleaning up, playing with your pet, guided imagery, volunteering, doing something creative such as writing, drawing, painting, sculpting, cooking, decorating, dancing, coloring, singing, playing an instrument, letting your feelings out in a healthy way such as talking, crying, stating how you are feeling out loud, journaling...

Deep breathing, deep relaxation, and meditation are well researched techniques known to have a significant impact on stress. There are countless deep breathing techniques, mindfulness and meditation apps, and all yoga classes typically end with a deep relaxation.

The following are some yogic based breathing techniques that can help create a sense of calm and reduce the impact of stress on your mind and body. Practice each one and then select the technique that works the most effectively for you and stick with it. With practice, you will find that you can impact the stress response very effectively with deep breathing techniques.

Deep Breathing

TO REDUCE STRESS AND CREATE CALM

Practice deep breathing for 5 minutes every day, slowly increasing to 10 minutes per day. The first is a review of diaphragmatic breathing. It is the foundation and can be your primary breathing practice. The other exercises listed here are options. All of these exercises are intended to create a calm mind and body.

1. Diaphragmatic Breathing: Feel your breath flowing in through your nose, filling your abdomen as you inhale (the abdomen expanding) and exhale through your nose feeling your belly button drawing back towards your spine. Let the breath be slow, smooth, deep and even. Watch the breath flowing in through the nose and out through the nose in your mind's eye.

2. 2 to 1 Breathing: count to 2, 3 or 4 (or more) as you inhale, and count to 4, 6 or 8 (or more) as you exhale, with your exhale becoming about twice as long as your inhale. It does not have to be exact, the intention is about lengthening each exhale. This practice develops focus and calms the nervous system.

3. 5x5 Breath: inhale to the count of 5, exhale to the count of 5. This creates about 6 breaths per minute, which is thought to be optimal for both physical and mental health. Breathing with a ticking clock can help with this technique.

4. 4-7-8 Breath: Inhale to the count of 4, hold your breath to the count of 7, place your tongue on your upper palette just behind your teeth, make an "o" shape with your mouth and exhale through the "o" to the count of 8. There will be a slight whooshing sound as you exhale. Repeat 4 times, do twice a day. You can work up to 8 breaths two times a day. This technique creates an overall sense of calm when practiced regularly and is a great way to prepare for meditation or for sleep.

5. So-Hum Breath: as you inhale say "so" to yourself in your mind, as you exhale say "hum" to yourself in your mind. Continue for several minutes or longer to help focus your attention and quiet your mind.

Try each of these exercises and determine which one works best in terms of creating a sense of calm in both mind and body. Once you select one, commit to practicing it daily for 5 minutes over the next week and reflect on your experience in the following chart:

Date	Breathing Practice Used	Minutes Practiced	How You feel Before the Practice	How You Feel Following the Practice
Example: Day 1: 9/12/17	2:1 Breathing	5	Stressed, anxious, overwhelmed	Calm, more relaxed, fewer anxious thoughts
Day 1:				
Day 2:				
Day 3:				
Day 4:				
Day 5:				
Day 6:				
Day 7:				

Reflect on your experience with adding a daily breathing practice here:

What changes did you notice in your mood?

_____

_____

_____

What changes did you notice in your energy?

_____

_____

_____

What surprised you the most?

_____

_____

_____

What else did you notice about the impact of breathing on you mentally and physically?

_____

_____

_____

_____

Will you continue this practice, why or why not?

_____

_____

_____

If it is difficult to practice breathing independently, find a class, an app, or guided practice to help create consistency. All yoga classes incorporate a focus on the breath and generally will teach specific deep breathing techniques. On my website, you can find other deep breathing and relaxation resources: www.wholisticfoodtherapy.com. Apps such as Insight Timer, Stop Think Breathe, and Headspace all have guided practices as well, just to name a few.

Breathing to help manage stress is so wonderful because it is always available, it does not cost a thing and with consistent practice it has a fairly immediate impact. Keep going with it in any way that works for you and notice the changes in your mood, your energy and your body.

Self-Care

Self-care is hard. If you are like most busy, stressed-out people, you probably place your needs near the bottom of your daily to-do list, if they are even on your list at all. What will often end up happening is that time runs out. Another day goes by without implementing a self-care practice. *Stop doing this!*

If you are over planning, try to be realistic as to what the self-care action will be, the time it will take, and *make it happen*.

This is *your* health, *your* well-being and *your* future. There may be challenging feelings that come up when you tell your family you have to spend an hour away from them, or tell a friend no you cannot help them with something they are asking of you. This may feel selfish at first and guilty feelings may arise. Guilt is a helpful emotion only if you have done something wrong. If you have not done something wrong, you can allow that emotion to move on; let it go.

Taking care of yourself is not selfish. Taking care of yourself is essential to living a healthy life. Taking care of yourself is self-preservation and when you do it you create the opportunity to live mindfully and vibrantly.

Talk to your family, your friends, anyone who will listen to you about your goals and what you are trying to accomplish and why. When you communicate with others you will hopefully get the support you need to make yourself, your health, and your life a priority.

Find the self-care practices that restore your energy, that help you feel good from the inside out. Use them as often as possible. The next exercise is about having a list available for taking care of yourself, as well having options that are not food based to cope more effectively with stress. It is all about nourishing yourself from the inside out, feeling rejuvenated and an opportunity to find pleasure, joy and relaxation in your life.

Positive Nourishment List

Create a list of things you enjoy, that you view as a treat, and that bring you a sense of fulfillment, calm, joy and nourishment that do not include food. When feeling down, stressed or triggered by negative emotions or situations, access your list and do something to help divert your energy away from stress eating. If you know you have a particularly stressful event on a particular day, choose something from your list to nourish yourself in a positive, kind and comforting manner. Challenge yourself to nourish yourself positively at least one time per day. You can refer to the list of coping strategies listed under the section *Coping with Stress* in this chapter for ideas.

1. _____

2. _____

3. _____

4. _____

5. _____

6. _____

7. _____

8. _____

9. _____

10. _____

11. _____

12. _____

13. _____

14. _____

15. _____

Place your Positive Nourishment List somewhere you will see it and practice using it anytime you feel stressed.

Stress AND Carbohydrates

Stress eating is pervasive. Oftentimes, the go-to foods to quell the stress in the moment are easy, processed carbohydrates. Carbs get a lot of press, and a lot of that press is bad. Here's the thing: carbohydrates are not the enemy. It is the *type* of carbohydrate that matters.

As with all of the nutrition information incorporated into this book, it is not intended to be scientific or advisory. There are no exact amounts for "perfect" health. It is information and a guide to awareness of how these foods and nutrients *make you feel*. Hopefully after chapter 3 you are eating a leafy green every day (and drinking lots of water). Technically, greens are carbs. All plant based foods essentially have a decent profile of carbohydrates.

Carbohydrates as a nutrient are not the enemy, they are essential to health. It is when they are taken out of their whole form that they become problematic. Refined, processed, and sugary carbohydrates are often where the challenges lie with carbs. The ironic thing is that these are typically the comforting foods you will choose when stressed-out!

Start becoming more aware of the amount of carbohydrates you are eating regularly without having to change anything, just to begin to build awareness. Once you are more self-aware you have an opportunity to make a choice. Spend a week reflecting daily on how your current carbohydrate consumption makes you feel.

If stress or emotional eating is a struggle for you, chances are you may not trust yourself with food. You may not trust your intuition when it comes to portions, what to eat, or what not to eat. A big part of this process is listening to your body, making peace with food, and trusting your intuition. You are the expert on your body. Practice listening and this will lead to healing your relationship with food, as well as with yourself.

Carbohydrates and Self-Awareness

Notice where you get the majority of your carbohydrates on a daily basis and write about the carbohydrates you take in regularly (reading labels, processed vs whole grain, etc.):

_____

_____

_____

How do you feel after eating these foods?

_____

_____

_____

How is your energy after eating these foods?

_____

_____

_____

Do you find yourself emotionally/stress eating carbohydrates? _____

If yes, the following exercise will help to explore these cravings and give you an opportunity to use an intervention from your Positive Nourishment List to practice releasing your stress in a healthy, non-food way.

Putting Your Positive Nourishment List into Action

The next time you have a craving that is driven by stress, use this exercise to intervene, using your Positive Nourishment List.

What are you craving?

_____

Why do you feel this particular food will help ease your stress?

_____

_____

_____

Do you believe this, why or why not?

_____

_____

_____

Choose something from your Positive Nourishment List to do instead, write it here:

_____

_____

How do you feel after completing the option from your list, how did it impact your craving?

_____

_____

_____

_____

_____

Can you commit to using your Positive Nourishment List to help reduce incidents of stress eating, why or why not and what can help you try?

_____

_____

_____

_____

_____

This list can be very useful in helping create lasting behavioral change with how you manage your stress. The more that you decrease incidents of stress eating, the more empowered you will feel and motivated to remain on your path towards making peace with food.

Write here how you will continue to empower yourself to use your Positive Nourishment List to cope with stress in a different manner than turning to food:

_____

_____

_____

_____

_____

_____

_____

_____

_____

Mindfulness and Nutrient Awareness

Choose a meal or snack and spend time observing your food. Ask yourself what it has to offer you. Specifically, notice the nutrients is has to offer: fiber, protein, vitamins, minerals, carbohydrate, fat, and *taste*. Ideally your snack or meal will have a variety of nutrients, and a high profile of those nutrients.

Yes, *taste* is included as a nutrient here. If your food does not taste good to you, it is unlikely that you will feel satisfied. You want the food you eat to be pleasurable. However, you do not want food to be your primary source of pleasure in your life, or for food to be a substitute for pleasure you are lacking.

Example of asking your food: *What do you have to offer me?* If you are holding an apple, it offers fiber, vitamins, minerals, carbohydrates and taste. If you are holding a doughnut, it has carbohydrate and taste.

If you ask your food, snack, or meal what it has to offer you, and the *only* thing it has to offer is taste or carbohydrate, there is a chance this food may not be something you want to choose to eat regularly. While there are indeed times when you will choose to eat that food just for taste, you just want to be clear that when you do make that choice *it is not an emotional choice.*

You will have the opportunity to investigate this more deeply in the next chapter. But for now, just begin with one meal or snack and ask these questions to your food:

-What do you have to offer me?
-Does this food choice align with my goal of improving my relationship with food?
-How will this choice make me feel later?

For the next week, practice this with one meal or snack every day and reflect on your experience in the following chart:

Date	Meal/Snack	Questions You Used	Impact on Your Choices
Example: Day 1: 9/12/17	Breakfast	What do you have to offer me? How will this choice make me feel later?	It made me feel good to think about the food I was about to eat offering protein, vitamins and minerals. I knew that I would stay satisfied until lunch.
Day 1:			
Day 2:			
Day 3:			
Day 4:			
Day 5:			
Day 6:			
Day 7:			

Reflect on this exercise here:

What changes did you notice in your relationship with food?

_____

_____

_____

What changes did you notice in your food choices?

_____

_____

_____

What surprised you the most?

_____

_____

_____

What else did you notice about the impact of asking your food what it has to offer you?

_____

_____

_____

How will you continue to use this practice and incorporate it into you daily life?

_____

_____

_____

_____

_____

_____

_____

_____

_____

CHAPTER FIVE

Dealing With Your Deal Maker

HEALING YOUR RELATIONSHIP WITH YOURSELF

"You may believe that you are responsible for what you do, but not for what you think. The truth is that you are responsible for what you think, because it is only at this level that you can exercise choice. What you do comes from what you think." -Marianne Williamson

By now, progress is getting made. You are beginning to feel more confident about your choices and growth. You are becoming more trusting of yourself, listening to your body and your intuition. Things are going so great! Then suddenly you might find that you fall back into old patterns and behaviors.

You may notice that you have essentially *talked yourself* into these choices. But you have been working so hard, doing so well, and feeling so good. A slip backwards happens and then what? You might say to yourself:

-Why bother?

-I knew this wouldn't work.

-I have tried so many things before, why would I think this would work?

You might also realize that you talked yourself into those old behaviors. How did this happen? Who is that? Why would this happen?

You could call this part of yourself the *Deal Maker*. You might find that you have an internal tendency to sabotage yourself, or an internal Deal Maker that attempts to get around your plans and goals essentially decreasing your motivation. This Deal Maker bargains internally to foil plans and goals for health and wellness.

Here is an example of how the Deal Maker works:

You plan to wake up and exercise before work. The alarm goes off, the Deal Maker says:

-I will exercise after work.

-I will skip breakfast to make up the calorie difference.

-I will have a light lunch today.

What actually happens for each of these options is often just another deal. A deal that leads to pacifying yourself into planning to exercise *tomorrow*, and then *tomorrow*, and then *tomorrow*. And before you know it you feel defeated and back into the: *Why bother?* mentality.

Another common statement the Deal Maker will use is the word *DESERVE*. It will say: "You had a hard day you *deserve* _____(insert your own word here)." It will convince you that you deserve what you are craving. You deserve to skip the gym. You deserve to buy those shoes. You deserve to have another cookie. You deserve whatever it is trying to convince you into feeling that you deserve. However, it usually is not the case, not in your best interest, and not moving you in the direction of your goals; your *wholistic* vision.

What *is* true is that you *deserve* to feel good, to feel proud, and to feel confident and strong. You *deserve* to make peace with food and in turn with yourself. You *deserve* to make healthy choices and to achieve your goals. You *deserve* to live your vision.

Positive Deserving Self Statements

Here are examples of positive deserving statements:

-I deserve to live my vision.

-I deserve to feel healthy and confident.

-I deserve balance in my life.

Write your positive deserving statements here and practice stating them to yourself daily:

I deserve_____.

I deserve to feel _____.

I deserve _____ in my life.

Practice saying these deserving statements to yourself over the next week and log your experience in the following chart:

Date	Deserving Self Statement Used	How You Feel After Stating This to Yourself
Example: Day 1: 9/12/17	I deserve to live my vision.	More confidence and desire to follow through with my goals.
Day 1:		
Day 2:		
Day 3:		
Day 4:		
Day 5:		
Day 6:		
Day 7:		

Reflect on your experience of using these positive deserving statements for the past week:

_____

_____

_____

_____

_____

_____

_____

_____

_____

_____

_____

Notice how your internal Deal Maker works and you may see it plays into many areas of your life. Becoming aware of the Deal Maker can help to stop the negotiations and stick to your original plans more often.

Developing Comebacks for Your Deal Maker

Use the chart below to work through some common excuses your Deal Maker uses and the comebacks you can use to STOP the negotiations and feel empowered by your choices.

Common Deal Maker Excuses	The Comeback You Can Use
Example: I had a hard day, I deserve this piece of cake.	I deserve to feel empowered by working towards my goal.
Example: I already ate something "bad" today so what's the point?	Although I ate something I did not feel good about earlier, the rest of the day is a new opportunity to work towards my goals.
Example: I'll start tomorrow.	Today is the day to make the best choice possible.

Reflect on how it feels to recognize so many of the excuses your Deal Maker constantly uses to sabotage your goals:

_____

_____

_____

_____

_____

_____

_____

_____

_____

_____

_____

_____

_____

Motivation

What motivates you is what you need to have available to move towards your vision. Believing in the possibility that you can heal your relationship with food through healing your relationship with yourself is essential. Having what motivates you available will keep you focused when the Deal Maker strikes.

It is ideal to be motivated by internal healthy desires such as: to feel good about yourself, to improve your internal numbers such as: blood pressure, blood sugar, cholesterol and so on. Sometimes other factors may be motivating as well. Just try to allow your health and wellness to be somewhere in the mix of what motivates you.

Describe what motivates you:

_____

_____

_____

_____

_____

_____

_____

_____

Describe how you can use what motivates you to help you deal with your Deal Maker:

_____

_____

_____

_____

Your Deal Maker is a part of you, and therefore often talks to you in *your own voice*. It can be extremely seductive and extremely convincing. This process of understanding how your Deal Maker works will take time and consistent effort. The Deal Maker will try to creep in when you least expect it.

Begin to understand your Deal Maker's purpose. This could be fear of change, complacency, stress, exhaustion, boredom, etc. Learn to listen and change your internal dialogue. All of your thoughts can become a choice. All of your behaviors are a choice.

Opt for positive, constructive questions to yourself such as:

-Does this choice support my vision?

-How will this choice make me feel?

-Does this choice help me achieve my goal of developing a healthy relationship with food?

-Does this choice help me improve my relationship with myself?

These are important questions to consider as you come to terms with your Deal Maker. It is persistent and convincing. Use these questions as often as you can and practice using your Internal Strength to resist your Deal Maker!

Knowing Your Deal Maker

What does your Deal Maker look like? Create or find an image that represents your Deal Maker and create or attach it here:

MORE WAYS TO DEAL WITH THE *Deal Maker*

The Deal Maker can cause setbacks in progress. Setbacks are however, part of the process. The derailment can feel too frustrating, tiring or hopeless to get over and to move past.

Reframing negative thinking is very helpful as well as examining the impact of negative thoughts and Deal Maker thoughts on the whole of your being: mind, body and spirit.

With reframing, it is helpful to work towards a neutral or reality based thought.

For example:

Negative thought: *I have tried to change before and it did not work.*

Reframe: *Although I have tried to change before, this time I am using a different framework and I am accessing more support.*

Or: *Although I have tried in the past and did not feel successful that does not mean that I am incapable of change.*

Or: *There have been times that I have changed, however I just seem to focus on the times I have not.*

Practice reframing the following. Then use your own current negative thoughts and continue to practice.

Reframing Negative Thoughts

Negative thought: *Why bother?*

Reframe:_____

_____

Negative thought: *I have tried to change before and it did not work.*

Reframe:_____

_____

Negative thought: *I will never change.*

Reframe:_____

_____

Negative thought:

Reframe:_____

_____

Negative thought:

Reframe:_____

_____

Examining and Reframing Your Negative Thoughts

Negative thoughts get in the way of progress, and are often driven by the Deal Maker. Examining how your thoughts are impacting you is helpful. Determining whether or not your thoughts are useful to your growth is helpful. As you examine your thoughts you can reduce your negative thoughts and the discomfort of a setback.

Here is an example:

Negative thought: *Why bother?*

Emotions connected to the thought: *Hopelessness, Frustration, Fear*

Where in your body do you hold these emotions/tensions? *Gut and chest*

What is it doing to you to hold onto this thought or belief about yourself? *Holding onto this negative thought is probably holding me back from making progress towards my goals, causing some uncomfortable feelings, leaving me stuck in a negative self-defeating cycle.*

Is this thought useful to my growth and change? *NO.*

Reframe: *Although I feel hopeless now, I can complete an action step today to help me move forward towards my goals and create a reason to bother.*

Practice Here WITH YOUR OWN NEGATIVE AND SELF-DEFEATING THOUGHTS

1. Negative thought:_____

_____

Emotions connected to the thought: _____

_____

Where in your body do you hold these emotions/tensions? _____

_____

What is it doing to you to hold onto this thought or belief about yourself?

_____

Is this thought useful to your growth and change? _____

_____

Reframe:_____

_____

2. Negative thought:_____

_____

Emotions connected to the thought: _____

_____

Where in your body do you hold these emotions/tensions? _____

_____

What is it doing to you to hold onto this thought or belief about yourself?

_____

Is this thought useful to your growth and change? _____

_____

Reframe:_____

_____

3. Negative thought:_____

_____

Emotions connected to the thought: _____

_____

Where in your body do you hold these emotions/tensions? _____

_____

What is it doing to you to hold onto this thought or belief about yourself?

_____

Is this thought useful to your growth and change? _____

_____

Reframe:_____

_____

Continue practicing this. One day you will notice that you are asking your-self if a thought is useful without having to go through all of the steps. Soon after that you will be able to reframe your negative, self-defeating thoughts more and more easily. Remember that you get good at what you practice. Keep using these tools to manage your mind and deal with your Deal Maker!

CHAPTER SIX
Emotional Eating
RECOGNIZING YOUR TRIGGERS AND UNDERSTANDING THE FOOD-MOOD CONNECTION

"He who knows others is wise. He who knows himself is enlightened. We don't reach enlightenment by going into the bright places in our lives, but by going into the dark places." —Carl Jung

Emotional eating is extremely common as the food-mood connection is immensely strong and intensely satisfying. At some point food became a coping skill, and as previously discussed in chapter 4, stress eating is pervasive. Any emotion can be a trigger. Anything can be a trigger.

Throughout this chapter, you will spend time familiarizing yourself with and exploring your triggers. You will have opportunities to reflect on them as well as developing a deeper understanding of your emotional cravings. Emotional cravings versus food cravings will be explored. Food cravings are purely a desire for the food, not for an emotional release.

Triggers are complex and just the sight, smell, or talk about food can cause the brain to get fixated on a food. Often these external triggers can be addressed in a different manner than the food-mood connection, which is an internal experience. Internal triggers that are related to food often run very deep.

Food may have been used as a reward or punishment when you were a child. This experience will have varying effects on you and your relationship with food into adulthood. Being told to clean your plate because others are starving involves emotional eating as well as not being encouraged to listen to your body-specifically your hunger and full sensations. Experiencing the comfort of being cooked your favorite meal implies that food is love. This may not necessarily be a bad thing, unless you began to associate food with love, and then it evolves into an emotional craving. These are all extremely common. If any of these examples reflect your experience, they may have impacted you deeply or they may have not. There are opportunities to explore your personal experiences throughout this chapter.

Food can be used as a coping strategy for *any* emotion; comfortable or uncomfortable. Food might be a friend when you feel lonely or something to do when you are bored. Food can be calming to eat when you are anxious or act as a motivator if you are procrastinating. Food can be linked to a certain activity enhancing pleasure or focus such as studying or watching a movie. It can be a celebration and it can be there to comfort you when feeling sad or down.

EXERCISE ONE
Your Food Story

Everyone has a story about how their relationship with food became dysfunctional. How emotions and stress got tangled up with your food choices. Journal here about your food story, your history with food and the messages both *direct*: (Clean your plate, there are other children starving) or indirect: (Watching a family member put themselves on diets and restricting their food intake, or a family member making self-deprecating comments about themselves such as: *my thighs are too big*.) Write your story here:

_____

_____

_____

_____

_____

_____

Reflect on your food story. What stands out to you the most?

_____

_____

_____

_____

Any "aha" moments? Describe them here:

_____

_____

_____

_____

What can you take from your increased awareness moving forward to help guide you towards making peace with food?

_____

_____

_____

_____

Food AND Emotions

Experiencing uncomfortable emotions is typically undesirable. For us humans, the tendency is to seek pleasure and avoid discomfort. Try to approach emotions from a different perspective. This process is mindful in nature and encourages *witnessing* the emotion and understanding why it has arisen.

Witnessing is observing the emotion and exploring it without getting caught into the story behind it. Witnessing avoids getting stuck on the roller coaster of the emotion. Witnessing is about being the observer of the emotion rather than the feeler of the emotion for that moment. This allows a different perspective. When you allow yourself to change your perspective you create an opportunity to change your response to the emotion.

Consider emotions as *information*. An emotion such as anger may be an indicator that you are not comfortable with the way you are being treated. Jealousy may be an indicator that you are feeling insecure in a relationship. When working with emotions and becoming more emotionally aware, try to view emotions in this way and frame them in a manner so you can learn about your experience.

Often as humans we want to transcend certain emotions, such as jealousy, greed or anger. However, we are all subject to any emotional trigger. If you can view emotions as information about your experience and learn from the emotion, you can then react accordingly. You may find that you hold on to less emotional baggage and experience more emotional freedom and self-awareness.

Journaling about emotions can be very useful to help express them and understand them more fully. In the following exercises, you will have an opportunity to explore your emotions through writing and mandala drawing. Allow yourself time when you can fully experience your emotional world and have time for reflection.

Coping With Emotions

For each emotion listed, write a *non-food* based coping strategy you can try to cope with the emotion more effectively. This is another opportunity to use your Positive Nourishment List or try one of the examples listed, or come up with your own:

Anxiety (coping skill examples: reframing fear based thoughts, deep breathing, guided relaxation/meditation, talk about it with someone you trust, journal, focus on gratitude...)

_____

_____

Anger (coping skill examples: scream into a pillow, exercise with the intention of releasing your anger, breathe, meditate, talk about it with someone you trust, journal, be kind to yourself...)

_____

_____

Sadness (coping skill examples: cry, journal, breathe, watch a funny show or movie, talk with someone you trust about how you are feeling...)

_____

_____

Loneliness (coping skill examples: call a friend, read, journal, join a book club, go to a meet up group, talk to someone you trust about how you feel...)

_____

_____

Guilt (coping skill examples: ask yourself, have I done something wrong? If not consider why you feel guilty and if it is an appropriate emotional response to the situation, journal, talk to someone you trust about how you feel...)

_____

_____

Happy (coping skill examples: do something you enjoy, reminisce, smile, spread your joy with others...)

_____

_____

Boredom (coping skill examples: find a new hobby, create something, dance, read, clean, call a friend, listen to music, make music, take a walk, exercise, catch up on work...)

_____

_____

Upset (coping skill examples: journal, cry, talk with someone you trust about how you feel, if someone has made you feel upset talk to them about it...)

_____

Unfulfilled (coping skill examples: journal about what brings you joy, review your vision for your life, make a new vision board, create anything, volunteer, see a career counselor, talk with someone you trust about how you feel, find an avenue for spirituality in your life...)

_____

_____

Nervous (coping skill examples: journal, talk with someone you trust about how you feel, breathe, listen to a guided relaxation/meditation, meditate, take a walk, practice gratitude...)

_____

_____

Fearful (coping skill examples: breathe, pray, share your fears with someone you trust, reframe your fear thought, journal...)

_____

_____

Hopeless (coping skill examples: talk with someone you trust about how you are feeling, keep a gratitude journal, breathe, meditate, read an inspirational book, use an affirmation of hope...)

_____

_____

Disappointed (coping skill examples: practice mindfulness, journal, talk to someone you trust about how you are feeling, keep or review a gratitude journal...)

_____

Uncomfortable (coping skill examples: journal, exercise/move, remove your-self from the situation if possible, set boundaries with those that make you uncomfortable, practice mindfulness staying present with the discomfort, witness it, if possible let it go...)

_____

_____

Embarrassed (coping skill examples: make a joke, cry, breathe, practice mindfulness, journal, share your experience and hear that others have prob-ably been through something similar...)

_____

_____

List other emotions you tend use food to cope with, and coping strategies you could try to be with, deal with or express the emotion without food:

_____

_____

Along your path of making peace with food, understanding, feeling and coping with emotions may be one of the most difficult elements of the jour-ney. This is a process and will take time. Being mindful, tuning into your in-ternal witness and asking yourself what is true in the moment is helpful to remain present with your emotions. Developing acceptance of what is true in this moment will help to deepen your experience of the moment and re-lease the discomfort of wishing for what is not true.

When you wish for what is not true, you suffer. When you align with what is true you can find acceptance and peace. With consistent effort to facili-tate this positive change of making peace with food, you are well on your way to growth and change.

Developing Awareness of Specific Food-Mood Connections

If these exercises related to feeling your feelings are overwhelming at first, use timed journaling. Start with one minute and increase as you are comfortable. Timed journaling can help you not get stuck in any one emotion. When the timer goes off you can move on, turn the page, and let it go.

Spend some time reflecting on your food-mood connection and how you might be using food to soothe any emotion. **Describe how emotional eating impacts you here:**

_____

_____

_____

_____

_____

_____

What emotion do you find that you turn to food for soothing or coping with the most?

_____

_____

_____

What is another coping strategy you could try when you are experiencing or overwhelmed by this emotion?

_____

_____

The next time you experience this emotion spend time writing about what it is like for you to experience this emotion here. Notice where you experience this emotion in your body and in your thoughts. Allow yourself to be fully present with the emotion:

_____

_____

_____

_____

_____

_____

_____

_____

_____

_____

Creative Expression of Emotion

Using line, shape, color, and form, use the mandala to express this feeling here:

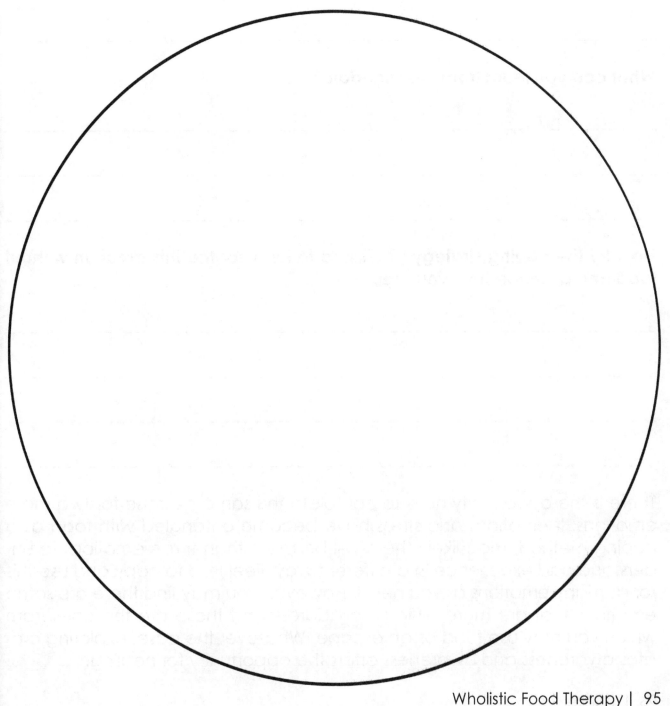

Mandala Title: _____

What stands out to you the most in your drawing?

_____

_____

_____

What can you learn from this mandala?

_____

_____

_____

Now try the coping strategy you listed to help soothe this emotion without food and describe how you feel:

_____

_____

_____

There is the opportunity here to complete this same exercise for two more emotions. If emotions and stress have become entangled with food as a coping method, most likely there will be more than three emotions to understand and experience in a different way. Feel free to copy and use this for as many emotions as you need. However, you may find there are some emotions that are more difficult to address and those are the ones from which you may use food as an escape. Whatever the case, exploring creates awareness and awareness offers the opportunity for healing.

EXERCISE FIVE

Developing Awareness of Specific Food-Mood Connections

What is another emotion that you find that you go to food for soothing or coping?

_____

What is a different coping strategy you could try when you are experiencing or overwhelmed by this emotion?

_____

_____

The next time you experience this emotion spend time writing about what it is like for you to experience this emotion here. Notice where you experience this emotion in your body as well as in your thoughts. Be fully present with the emotion:

_____

_____

_____

_____

_____

_____

Creative Expression of Emotion

Using line, shape, color, and form, use the mandala to express this feeling here:

Mandala Title: _____

What stands out to you the most in your drawing?

_____

_____

_____

What can you learn from this mandala?

_____

_____

_____

Now try the coping strategy you listed to help soothe this emotion without food and describe how you feel:

_____

_____

_____

How can you use what you have learned about yourself through your drawing and through the coping strategy to continue to grow in your self-awareness?

_____

_____

_____

Developing Awareness of Specific Food-Mood Connections

What is another emotion that you find that you go to food for soothing or coping?

_____

What is a different coping strategy you could try when you are experiencing or overwhelmed by this emotion?

_____

_____

The next time you experience this emotion spend time writing about what it is like for you to experience this emotion here. Notice where you experience this emotion in your body as well as in your thoughts. Be fully present with the emotion:

_____

_____

_____

_____

_____

Creative Expression of Emotion

Using line, shape, color, and form, use the mandala to express this feeling here:

Mandala Title: _____

What stands out to you the most in your drawing?

_____

_____

_____

What can you learn from this mandala?

_____

_____

_____

Now try the coping strategy you listed to help soothe this emotion without food and describe how you feel:

_____

_____

_____

Other emotions may also need some reflection and having a coping skill handy will make it more likely to create a new habit pattern from soothing with food to soothing with a healthy coping strategy.

Continue using the mandalas if you find them helpful in exploring and expressing your feelings. There are more in the back of the book in the resources to use as needed.

Understanding Cravings

Cravings are different than triggers. However, they can overlap. A craving can signal that the body's nutrients are out of balance, that you are dehydrated, that your diet is too restrictive or repetitive. Cravings can also indicate that you are angry, sad, happy (or any emotion) and associate that emotion with a certain food.

Try not to think of cravings as good or bad, they just are, they happen, they are information your body and mind are trying to communicate to you.

It is what you do about the craving, how you investigate it and how you cope with it that will make all the difference.

Developing a cravings protocol will help you determine what to do when overwhelmed by a craving. It is empowering yourself with a plan, leading you to more mindful choices and creating a healthier relationship with food.

In order to develop a workable and effective protocol for cravings, think about what might be effective for you in the moment of a craving. Having three simple things to do in the moment of a craving will help you make the best choice possible.

Here is an example of a cravings protocol:

1. Have a glass of water and set your timer for 5 minutes, do not eat during the 5 minutes.

2. Do something on your positive nourishment or coping skills for emotions lists.

3. 1 minute of deep breathing.

After completing these steps, reflect on the craving.

Is it still there? If so, is it an emotional craving or not? If not, can you have a healthy version of what you are craving? For example, if you are craving something sweet could you have a piece of fruit or a homemade healthy smoothie? Can you find sweetness in your life in a non-food way?

If you still cannot shake the craving and it does not seem to be an emotionally driven craving, allow yourself to eat what you are craving. Allow this to be a planned non-emotional experience of enjoying the food you are craving. Portion it out, enjoy it, savor it, notice the textures, the aromas, and be mindful with each bite.

EXERCISE NINE
Coping With Cravings

The next time you have a craving, reflect on the experience here.

Describe your craving. What do you want? Why do you think you want it? How does it feel in your body to want this food?

_____

_____

_____

_____

Is there an emotion that needs to be expressed or that you are avoiding? If yes, describe the emotional connection:

_____

_____

_____

_____

_____

What is a cravings protocol you can use to move past the craving?

1. _____

2. _____

3. _____

Now, try it.

What is your experience after trying this protocol?

_____

_____

_____

_____

If you choose to eat what you are craving describe how you feel here:

_____

_____

_____

_____

If there are any negative experiences emotionally, digestively, or physically, list them here. However, try to just list them as facts, not as failures. This is all about building self-awareness, without it, no change will be possible:

_____

_____

_____

_____

Describe how you will use your cravings protocol moving forward in your process of making peace with food:

_____

_____

_____

_____

CHAPTER SEVEN
Clearing The Clutter of Trigger Foods
STRATEGIES ALONG THE PATH

"The thing you fear most has no power. Your fear of it is what has the power. Facing the truth really will set you free." -Oprah Winfrey

Trigger foods are foods that are difficult to eat within the portion size. They can cause cravings, and they can be hard to put away. These foods are often devoid of any nutrient value.

One primary trigger food for many people is sugar.

Sugar is trouble. It seems it is in just about everything which makes it so difficult to avoid. Once you eat it, it often asks for more. Sugar is one of the most common trigger foods for those that struggle with an emotional attachment to food. Sugar can be one of the hardest to clear out of your daily diet.

Sugar is known to be a highly addictive substance. This is where it becomes complicated. Sugar stimulates the pleasure center in the brain, making it desirable just as it is. When that becomes intertwined with an avoidance of emotion or when presented with a stressor, it can be very dangerous. Due to this addictive nature, sugar is a challenge to change when it has been adapted as a coping skill for stress or uncomfortable emotions.

Often when attempting to cut out sugar or other trigger foods, it can bring up fears. Fear of not finding pleasure in food. Fear of deprivation. Fear of change. Fear of the unknown. This may sound a little dramatic, however it is helpful to be prepared for any fears that will arise as you work through this chapter addressing foods that are triggering, especially sugar.

The American Heart Association recommends that women *consume only*

24 *grams of added sugar per day,* men **36** grams and children **12** grams. One teaspoon of cane sugar is equivalent to 4 grams of added sugar and one teaspoon of honey is 5 grams.

These added sugar numbers can add up rapidly. You can imagine that many people are eating well out of this suggested range of added sugar as just a typical 12-ounce can of soda contains 35 grams of added sugar, a 20-ounce can contain up to 65 grams of added sugar. While soda might seem obvious, sugar finds its way into so many of the foods we eat on a daily basis. Often there is added sugar in tomato sauce, yogurt, sliced deli meat, just to name a few common foods. To locate added sugar content, refer to the nutritional information section on the package where sugar is listed.

The foods we consume daily can make it all the more difficult to eat health-fully and to clear the excess sugar out of your life.

EXERCISE ONE

How Does Sugar Make You Feel?

Understanding how any food makes you feel, before, during, and after you eat it helps create a healthy relationship with food through self-awareness. This revisits the concept of trusting yourself and your intuition with food. Awareness is the first step to making a conscious choice or decision. Spend time with this exercise reflecting on how sugar makes you feel, physically, mentally, emotionally and energetically before during and after consuming it.

The next time you eat a sugary food or drink a sugary beverage describe how you feel just before eating/drinking it:

_____

_____

_____

_____

Describe how you felt while eating/drinking it:

_____

_____

_____

_____

Describe how feel after eating/drinking it:

_____

_____

_____

_____

EXERCISE TWO
Sugar Awareness

Over the next week, without changing anything in your diet, log the added sugar you consume here:

For this purpose, you do not need to calculate sugars in raw or cooked fruits and vegetables. Focus on packaged foods and any added sugar that you use, such as a teaspoon of sugar in your coffee or honey in your tea.

Date	Added Sugar Grams
Example: Day 1: 9/12/17	52
Day 1:	
Day 2:	
Day 3:	
Day 4:	
Day 5:	
Day 6:	
Day 7:	

Did anything surprise you about the amount of added sugar you take in on a daily basis?

_____

_____

What foods have added sugar that surprised you the most?

_____

_____

Awareness is the first step. Once you become aware of the amount of sugar in your diet, you can decide what changes can be made and what you feel is a reasonable amount for you.

If you found that you use, for example, three teaspoons of cane sugar in your coffee in the morning, would it be possible to cut back to two and half teaspoons for a week, and then two teaspoons the following week? These small changes can add up to a big difference in your health and wellness.

What is an average amount of added sugar that you feel would be healthy for you to consume on a daily basis?

_____

Where can you reduce your sugar intake?

_____

_____

When will you begin this reduction? _____

How long do you want this sugar reduction to take?_____

Do any fear thoughts come up for you around reducing your sugar intake? If so, what are they?

_____

_____

What would it mean to you for sugar to no longer soothe your emotions, and to make choices based on your intuition and goals?

_____

_____

_____

The challenge with sugar is that it often asks for more. Let's say that recently you have not taken in a significant amount of added sugar on a daily basis. Then one day you have a cookie after dinner. The next night you do not have a cookie nearby. You are not even hungry. However, you find yourself thinking about how you would like to have a cookie. This is the sugar asking for itself! It is troublesome, and the more you respond to these cravings, the more places you will find sugar infiltrating your daily diet.

Clearing out the sugar may be difficult, and you may not use the 24 (woman)/36 (man) grams as your guideline. You might use 30, or 40 grams of added sugar as your guideline. You might find that you feel healthy at those numbers, and that is about listening to your body. It is more about being conscious of the amount of added sugar you are taking in regularly and its effects on your relationship with food. It is not about being perfect, it is about awareness, choice, and listening to your body while working towards your goals.

While sugar may be the most common and pervasive trigger food, other foods can certainly be trigger foods as well. Often fried foods, packaged snack foods, processed foods and salty foods can trigger the desire to eat more and cause you to get away from being intuitive about your food choices.

How Do Other Trigger Foods Make You Feel?

What are your trigger foods?

_____

_____

The next time you eat this trigger food, describe how you feel just before consuming it:

_____

_____

Describe how you felt while consuming it:

_____

_____

_____

Describe how feel after consuming it:

_____

_____

_____

Knowing Your Inner Strength

Your Inner Strength is growing and becoming even stronger as you engage with this process of making peace with food. You are developing your Inner Strength with each exercise and it is what you can access to deal effectively with your Deal Maker. Reflect on the responses related to your trigger foods.

Create or find an image that represents your Inner Strength, how you *want* to be with your trigger foods and create or attach it here:

Grocery Shopping for Success

What claims does your Deal Maker make to get you to purchase trigger foods at the grocery store?

Common Claims Your Deal Maker Uses at the Grocery Store	Your Comeback to Help You Stick to Your List
Example: You deserve a treat	Today I choose to stick to my list

The list could possibly go on and on. This is the internal dialogue that may occur for you at the grocery store, a restaurant, or *anywhere* where you have to make a choice regarding food. Having your comebacks ready will be the best place to start. Remind yourself of your Inner Strength. That is the place within you where your comebacks will arise.

Other tools to employ at the grocery store:

Make a LIST!

Most likely you always have a list. It's just that some of those trigger foods are not on the list, and yet they still find their way into the shopping basket. So more importantly than making this list is: *sticking to the list!*

While yes, having the list is an important tool and first step other tools will be helpful at the store. Aligning with your Inner Strength prepared with comebacks for your Deal Maker and doing a visualization before even stepping foot into the store can be tremendously helpful. If there is even the slight chance of wavering in your decision making, this visualization step can be extremely effective.

Visualization

First, make your list. Allow your breath to become relaxed and steady. Before leaving to go to the store, close your eyes and visualize yourself in your mind's eye at the store placing only the items on your list into your shopping cart.

Notice how this feels. Be aware of any resistance. Remain aware and maintain your focus.

Now visualize yourself in your mind's eye going through the check-out purchasing only the items on your list.

Notice how this feels. Be aware of any resistance or fears. Remain aware and focused.

Now visualize yourself in your mind's eye at home, putting away the food, with no trigger foods present.

Notice how this feels.

Spend some time reflecting on your experience with this visualization exercise:

_____

_____

_____

_____

Did anything surprise you about this visualization? _____

_____

What emotions were present?

_____

The next time you go grocery shopping, try this exercise before leaving, and again once you arrive at the store. Reflect on how it goes for you here:

_____

_____

_____

Did anything surprise you about your experience?

_____

_____

What emotions were present?

_____

Did this exercise help with creating awareness of your Deal Maker and how hard it works at the grocery store? Were you able to use your comebacks, to stay in touch with your Inner Strength?

_____

_____

_____

Commit to using this exercise and notice how it impacts your decisions and choices at the grocery store. Use it anywhere you will have to make a choice regarding food.

EXERCISE SEVEN

Combatting Sugar Cravings by Finding Sweetness in Non-Food Ways

Aside from food, what makes you feel good, sweet, positive, and full of joy?

_____

_____

_____

Commit yourself to engaging in these activities regularly. They might be stress relievers from your Positive Nourishment List, coping strategies, or something else altogether.

When craving a sweet, choose something from this list above and reflect on your experience here:

_____

_____

_____

_____

_____

Being Kind To Yourself

Being kind to yourself is another way to find sweetness in your life without food.

Positive affirmations are a useful tool to help yourself feel positive. Saying kind words from your heart to yourself can make a big difference in how you feel.

Examples of positive affirmations:
-I accept myself unconditionally.
-I love myself unconditionally.
-I am just right just as I am.
-I am here for a reason.
-There is a purpose to my life.
-I strive to be the best person I can be.
-My willpower is continuing to strengthen.
-I am confident and strong.
-My life is unfolding just as it is supposed to be.
-I am becoming healthier every day.
-I can calm my mind and relax my body.
-I appreciate all that I have.
-I am all that I need.
-I am inspired to live my vision.
-I am creating a life that I love.

Write a positive affirmation from the list above, one that you developed or one you have found elsewhere that resonates with you that you can state to yourself daily, or at any moment to be kind to yourself, to turn your kindness inward:

_____

For the next week, state an affirmation to yourself daily and log your experience here:

Date	Affirmation Used	How You Feel After Stating it to Yourself
Example: Day 1: 9/12/17	There is a purpose to my life.	Hopeful
Day 1:		
Day 2:		
Day 3:		
Day 4:		
Day 5:		
Day 6:		
Day 7:		

How did it feel to use a positive affirmation daily?

_____

_____

Was there anything difficult about this practice?

_____

_____

_____

What shifts or changes did you notice?

_____

_____

_____

How did this practice impact your relationship with food?

_____

_____

_____

Will you continue with this practice, why or why not?

_____

_____

_____

Positive Affirmation Cards

Stating your positive affirmation regularly is helpful along your path to making peace with yourself. Having a visual reminder of your affirmation will allow you to pull from this positive energy when struggles arise. This is a creative exercise in having your affirmations available in card form to place in your visual space. You can place it in your wallet, by your bedside, or anywhere you will see them regularly. This visual reminder allows you to stay connected to your vision, to remain positive in your focus, and to concentrate on your ability to make peace with food as well as with yourself.

Materials:

Card stock or other thick paper, enough for 5 cards, or maybe more!

A selection of images that are inspirational to you

Glue

Scissors

Clear contact paper if desired

Process:

Cut your card stock to about 2x4 or 3x5 if it is not already sized

Write, or use cut out words to put your affirmation onto each card. You might just use one affirmation or several inspirational statements to have a deck of cards full of positivity!

On the back of each card draw, or glue images that match how you feel about the affirmation.

Once completed you can use the contact paper to protect them, this step is optional.

FOCUSING ON THE *Positive*

Often there is a tendency when working towards change to focus on what did not go well rather than on what did go well. Examples of focusing on the negative include: *I did not exercise today.* Or: *I ate that cookie today.* This creates disappointment and continued negative self-talk.

When your focus is on the negative, that will zap any energy and motivation you have created. The negative self-talk thought patterns of: *Why bother?* And: *I'll never change* can come in and sabotage your progress. This only perpetuates the negative cycle, and lack of motivation to believe in yourself.

When you place your focus on what went well, what you *did* do, it replenishes your energy and keeps you focused on the possibility of success. This possibility, this focus on the positive steps you did take, will help you remain focused. Focusing on the positive opens you up for more positive events to happen and ultimately for success. Examples of what *did* go well: *I did deep breathing for 5 minutes today.* Or: *I stated my affirmation today.* Or: *I had a serving of leafy greens today.* Reminding yourself of what *did* go well allows you to feel empowered to continue to move forward.

Seeing this list of what you *did* do, will remind you of the possibility of progress. Keeping a log of your progress and reflecting on it regularly will create encouragement and continued motivation for growth and change. These reminders of your progress create continued opportunities for healing and for feeling successful.

It seems as human beings we tend to notice and focus on what is going wrong rather than what is going well. This is a practice that takes time, energy, and a determined focus to develop. It is possible, even if your tendency is towards pessimism, or *especially* if your tendency is towards pessimism to change this tendency and create a more positive focus.

Use the following exercise to begin to develop positive self-talk and reflection upon what progress you are making in small incremental steps.

Think about this like building a muscle. If you do a strength building exercise, such as a plank pose only one time, your muscles will not develop. If you do a plank pose every day for several weeks, you will begin to notice a change in your strength. The same with shifting from a negative mindset to a positive mindset. Practice, repetition, consistency and dedication will allow this mental muscle grow!

EXERCISE TEN

Positive Daily Reflection Journal

"We can always choose to perceive things differently. We can focus on what's wrong in our life, or we can focus on what's right." -Marianne Williamson

Positive Self-Care Journal: Each day over the next week write down two self-care focused action steps you take that day. Anything that you do to support your mind and body. These are two things that helped you move towards your goals; your vision. As you reflect on these two actions, if negative or dismissive thoughts attempt to come into the forefront of your mind, return to focusing on what you *did* do to support your goals. This is a practice and takes time. With consistency, it is possible.

Date	Positive Daily Action Reflection
Example: Day 1: 9/12/17	Drank 8 glasses of water Went for a walk with my dog
Day 1:	
Day 2:	
Day 3:	
Day 4:	
Day 5:	
Day 6:	
Day 7:	

After completing this exercise, reflect on the impact of focusing daily on what went well, what you *did* do to support your goals each day:

_____

_____

_____

_____

CHAPTER EIGHT

Mindfulness and Food
THE POWER OF NON-JUDGMENT

"Breathing in, I calm body and mind. Breathing out, I smile. Dwelling in the present moment I know this is the only moment." -Thich Nhat Hanh

Mindful Eating is a thing. You may have read about it, taken a Mindful Eating course, or maybe even have tried it. It is very powerful to eat in a mindful way. It can also bring up a lot of emotion to be mindful, especially with food. Mindful Eating is simple, but not easy.

Mindfulness is paying attention from moment to moment with a non-judgmental awareness. Again, the concept seems to be simple enough, but it definitely is not easy. Mindfulness in fact, can be extremely challenging.

The most difficult part is keeping the mind focused in the present moment. The tendency of the mind is to wander. The mind typically moves rapidly from thought to thought. The mind is constantly fluctuating and really is only sifting through a few things: the past, the future, the story of me (our internal soap opera, or the I-maker), and judgmental thoughts.

These are all conditions of the mind that can cause discomfort, or any emotion, and then your body responds accordingly. In the circumstance of experiencing fear thoughts about the future (catastrophizing), the body responds accordingly. When stuck in regrets of the past, the body responds accordingly. When fantasizing about the stories about yourself that can be quite dramatic in the mind, the body responds accordingly. When judging or comparing yourself, yes, the body responds accordingly. All of these conditions of the mind can cause discomfort, mentally, physically, emotionally and spiritually.

So how do we begin to train the mind?

With a mindfulness practice.

What does this have to do with food?

Everything.

In order to live in the present moment, where life is unfolding and is truly the only moment that exists and never ends, you have to practice.

In order to make peace with food as well as with yourself, you need to be present and aware of what is occurring, mentally, emotionally and physically. Only then you can decide if this is how you want to be.

Mindless Eating

Understanding *mind**less*** eating helps to gain understanding of the importance of *mind**ful*** eating.

The following questions help to identify how mindful or mindless you might be while eating:

How often do you eat an entire meal and not remember eating even one bite, as if you were on autopilot?

_____

How often do you eat an entire serving of a snack or food item and think *I didn't mean to eat the whole thing?*

_____

How often do you eat while driving, watching TV, or surfing the internet?

_____

How often do you "clean your plate" just because?

_____

These are all examples of mind*less* eating.

How do you feel after any of these experiences of mindless eating?

_____

_____

_____

_____

EXERCISE ONE

Daily Mindful Practice

When beginning a mindfulness practice, it is useful to start with something mundane. Something simple. Something you do every day and do not have to think about.

Examples include: brushing your teeth, driving, taking a walk, taking a shower, folding laundry, or washing the dishes. Choose one of these, or something else that you do daily and tend to do mindlessly, on autopilot. Stick with the specific task for the entirety of this practice.

For the next week challenge yourself to practice being as focused as possible on one of these generally more mindless life tasks that you do every single day.

If you are not sure what to choose use brushing your teeth. It is typically something you do two times a day and for only a couple of minutes.

What task will you choose to practice being more mindful, to pay attention more intentionally? _____

When you take on this task, notice how often your mind wants to pull you in different directions and try to be aware of where it wants to take you (the varying fluctuations of the mind). The intention is to practice being present with the task, to pull away from the tendency to get lost in the fluctuations of the mind. The intention is self-awareness as well as creating an opportunity to be engaged with the power of the present moment.

Again, this is a challenging concept, and might prove to be extremely difficult at first.

Try to stay with it, to stay focused on this one task or activity and to stay presently focused and aware all throughout.

Becoming more aware of how much the mind wanders is a valuable process. Noticing how many negative thoughts you might have. Noticing how often you are stuck in a mind state that is not useful. Noticing when your thoughts are not helping to move you forward in the direction of positive growth and change. Becoming more aware of what is occurring mentally and the impact those thoughts have emotionally and physically is an empowering experience of creating more internal focus, self-awareness, and opens you to the ability to choose your thoughts.

Log your experience in the following chart:

Date	What Did You Notice?
Example: Day 1: 9/12/17	Used: Brushing teeth. I tried to focus on the taste of the toothpaste, the sound of the toothbrush. My mind wandered constantly and at the end I noticed I was lost in thought, but was able to return to brushing my teeth.
Day 1:	
Day 2:	
Day 3:	
Day 4:	
Day 5:	
Day 6:	
Day 7:	

After completing this week-long mindfulness challenge, reflect on your experience here:

What stands out to you the most?

_____

_____

What did you learn about your mind this week?

_____

_____

_____

What did you learn about yourself?

_____

_____

_____

Did it seem to get easier to focus throughout the week? _____

If it did, will you continue to use this as a practice? _____

Did you notice any changes in your ability to focus in other areas of your life? If so, where and how?

_____

_____

_____

Mindful Eating

Now that you are more aware of how your mind works and how easily the mind shifts into autopilot, you might now be more aware of the impact it has on you to be mindless. There is little to no use to living mindlessly, and a tremendously positive impact to living mindfully. You can now begin to grow your mindfulness practice into mindful eating.

You also might wonder about what to do with the daydreaming element, with how to think about the past or future. The emphasis is not on never allowing yourself to think about the past or future, to never daydream, it is about your intention. If you need to plan for the future, talking about it or thinking about it with intention *in the present moment* can be very beneficial.

The same concept is true with processing the past in order to learn and grow, or to reminisce in a way that feels good; that helps you savor a memory from the past. It is the intention you bring to the present moment that is important. The aimless movement of the mind can create discomfort and engage the stress response in your body mindlessly. This is not useful.

When eating in a mindless way, the stress response can be activated due to what might be occurring mentally and will impact digestion, how you feel, as well as how your body assimilates the nutrients in your food. Use the following exercise to begin a mindful eating practice.

EXERCISE TWO

Mindful Eating

Choose one meal or snack to eat mindfully every day for the next week. Commit yourself to allowing this to be time only for eating. No TV, no phone or internet, no reading, no distractions. Just eating.

Decide which meal or snack you will choose and begin by smelling your food. Really taking in the aromas. Eating slowly and intentionally. Chewing your food thoroughly. Tasting every bite. Place your utensils down between bites. Or, if eating with your hands, set your food down between bites. Notice the texture of the food in your mouth and every element of the taste.

Try to view your food as just food. Nothing else. No judgment. You are not labeling the food as good food or bad food. You are allowing yourself to taste your food thoroughly and notice its effects.

Log your experience in the following chart:

Date and Meal or Snack	What Did You Notice About Your Food?	What Was This Like For You?
Example: Day 1: 9/12/17 Breakfast	I enjoyed my smoothie and enjoyed the sweetness of the strawberries.	It was different. It felt weird to not watch TV. I was uncomfortable and my mind wanted to wander on and on about nothing.
Day 1:		
Day 2:		
Day 3:		
Day 4:		
Day 5:		
Day 6:		
Day 7:		

Reflect on your experience with mindful eating here:

What stands out to you the most?

_____

_____

What did you learn about your mind this week in relation to eating?

_____

_____

_____

What did you learn about yourself?

_____

_____

_____

Did it seem to get easier to focus throughout the week? _____

Will you continue to use this as a practice? _____

Did you notice any changes in focus in other areas of your life? If so, where and how?

_____

_____

_____

Mindful eating is very powerful. It helps to build more trust in your relationship with food, to eat more intuitively. Being mindful and eating intentionally allows you to be more aware of your hunger and full cues, how different foods make you feel, and increases the ability to savor and derive true pleasure from food, rather than emotional avoidance or fulfillment.

Awareness OF FULL AND EMPTY STATES

Recognizing hunger and full cues is a helpful element in developing a healthy relationship with food. This process requires the ability to be mindful.

Hunger Scale:

0= no hunger present

1= slight hunger present

2= mild hunger, could eat a snack

3= fairly hungry, stomach may be growling, ready for a meal

4= very hungry, stomach growling, possible headache, may be getting irritable or shaky

5= beyond hungry, full on *hangry*

Full Scale:

0= not at all full

1= not at all full, but aware of food in your stomach

2= slightly full, still could eat more

3= fairly full, may be helpful to wait 5-10 minutes and see if you are satiated

4= overly full, slightly uncomfortable or bloated

5= completely stuffed, very uncomfortable

Generally, it is best to eat when you are around a **3** on the hunger scale and stop eating around a **3** on the full scale.

This is intended to be a guide, not a hard and fast rule. Try not to judge the number as good or bad. Your number just indicates where you are so you can make a choice in the present moment based on how you feel physically. The more awareness you build with your body and its sensations, its ability to communicate, the more you will listen intuitively and trust yourself with food.

EXERCISE THREE

Paying Attention To Hunger and Full Cues

For the next week practice gauging how hungry you are before each meal or snack and how full you feel following each meal and each snack. Log your experience here:

Date	Meal/Snack	Hunger Level						Full Level					
	Breakfast	0	1	2	3	4	5	0	1	2	3	4	5
	Lunch	0	1	2	3	4	5	0	1	2	3	4	5
Day 1:	Dinner	0	1	2	3	4	5	0	1	2	3	4	5
	Snack	0	1	2	3	4	5	0	1	2	3	4	5
	Snack	0	1	2	3	4	5	0	1	2	3	4	5
	Snack	0	1	2	3	4	5	0	1	2	3	4	5
	Breakfast	0	1	2	3	4	5	0	1	2	3	4	5
	Lunch	0	1	2	3	4	5	0	1	2	3	4	5
Day 2:	Dinner	0	1	2	3	4	5	0	1	2	3	4	5
	Snack	0	1	2	3	4	5	0	1	2	3	4	5
	Snack	0	1	2	3	4	5	0	1	2	3	4	5
	Snack	0	1	2	3	4	5	0	1	2	3	4	5

Day 3:	Breakfast	0 1 2 3 4 5	0 1 2 3 4 5
	Lunch	0 1 2 3 4 5	0 1 2 3 4 5
	Dinner	0 1 2 3 4 5	0 1 2 3 4 5
	Snack	0 1 2 3 4 5	0 1 2 3 4 5
	Snack	0 1 2 3 4 5	0 1 2 3 4 5
	Snack	0 1 2 3 4 5	0 1 2 3 4 5
Day 4:	Breakfast	0 1 2 3 4 5	0 1 2 3 4 5
	Lunch	0 1 2 3 4 5	0 1 2 3 4 5
	Dinner	0 1 2 3 4 5	0 1 2 3 4 5
	Snack	0 1 2 3 4 5	0 1 2 3 4 5
	Snack	0 1 2 3 4 5	0 1 2 3 4 5
	Snack	0 1 2 3 4 5	0 1 2 3 4 5
Day 5:	Breakfast	0 1 2 3 4 5	0 1 2 3 4 5
	Lunch	0 1 2 3 4 5	0 1 2 3 4 5
	Dinner	0 1 2 3 4 5	0 1 2 3 4 5
	Snack	0 1 2 3 4 5	0 1 2 3 4 5
	Snack	0 1 2 3 4 5	0 1 2 3 4 5
	Snack	0 1 2 3 4 5	0 1 2 3 4 5
Day 6:	Breakfast	0 1 2 3 4 5	0 1 2 3 4 5
	Lunch	0 1 2 3 4 5	0 1 2 3 4 5
	Dinner	0 1 2 3 4 5	0 1 2 3 4 5
	Snack	0 1 2 3 4 5	0 1 2 3 4 5
	Snack	0 1 2 3 4 5	0 1 2 3 4 5
	Snack	0 1 2 3 4 5	0 1 2 3 4 5
Day 7:	Breakfast	0 1 2 3 4 5	0 1 2 3 4 5
	Lunch	0 1 2 3 4 5	0 1 2 3 4 5
	Dinner	0 1 2 3 4 5	0 1 2 3 4 5
	Snack	0 1 2 3 4 5	0 1 2 3 4 5
	Snack	0 1 2 3 4 5	0 1 2 3 4 5
	Snack	0 1 2 3 4 5	0 1 2 3 4 5

Reflect on your experience here:

What stands out to you the most?

_____

_____

What did you learn about yourself this week in relation to eating?

_____

_____

What did you learn about your hunger and full cues?

_____

_____

Do you trust yourself with food in a different way after this exercise, if so why?

_____

_____

_____

Did you notice any changes in your relationship with food this week, if so what?

_____

_____

_____

Non-judgment

Non-judgment is one of the primary elements of mindfulness. There is a big difference between noticing and judging. The following exercise will explore how you are with your food. When practicing mindful eating, be present with your food and notice its taste, texture and effects on your mind and body. Non-judgment is the ability to label food for what it is, not good or bad; just food. It is the ability to describe it without adding in emotions or judgments.

One of the fluctuations of the mind is judging. This can be as difficult to notice as it is to change. You might view food as calories, or as good or bad. These are judgements. You might say things or have thoughts such as: *I shouldn't eat that.* Or: *I've been bad today.* These thoughts create self-judgment and often negative self-talk and negative emotions.

Using non-judgment, practice viewing food for what it is without qualifying it. A piece of bread is just a piece of bread. A vegetable is just a vegetable. A dessert is just a dessert. This is a challenging exercise as your mind might try to pull you in other directions. Your mind will try to sneak in the judging thoughts. Awareness will grow. Practice is key.

The following is an exercise in non-judgment with food.

You will draw your food on the plate, or cut out images of food and glue them to the plate and try to just label your food for what it is. What are the facts? What is true? What are the specifics of the food, the qualities, flavors and nutrients, such as sweet, salty, pungent, bitter, spicy, cold, cool, warm, hot. Practice labeling specifically and it will help your mind move away from the loaded judgments of your typical internal dialogue in relation to food.

EXERCISE FOUR
Non-judgment and Food

On the plate below, draw or glue cut out images of your meal and begin to view your food from a place of non-judgment:

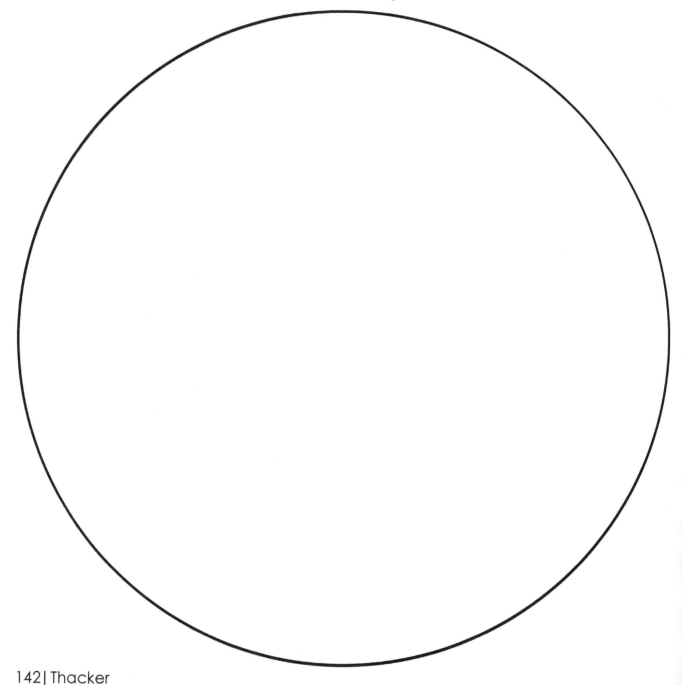

Describe your meal, the color, texture, names of the foods, nutrients in the food, tastes and qualities all just for exactly what they are:

_____

_____

_____

What was this like for you?

_____

_____

How difficult was it for you to not make judging statements about your food, from likes to dislikes or good to bad?

_____

_____

At your next meal practice this exercise with your actual food on your plate. State to yourself the descriptions of the food you are about to eat in this non-judgmental manner. Staying clear of qualifying statements. Be aware if your mind tries to create qualifying statements such as good or bad; positive or negative. Stay in the present moment and practice mindfully eating this meal.

Reflect on your experience here: **What did you notice?**

_____

_____

_____

Did anything surprise you about this experience?

_____

_____

_____

Did you notice any changes with your relationship with food following this exercise? If so, what did you notice?

_____

_____

_____

With anything in life, you get good at what you practice. If you have been practicing negative self-talk while eating, or judging your food choices, saying things to yourself such as: _I shouldn't eat this_, you are probably good at that negative perspective. If you have been excessively concerned about calories, you are probably pretty good at viewing food as calories and that indicates the food as being good or bad. Know that it will take time to get good at mindful eating. Practice mindful eating and it will feel more comfortable, more natural over time. Be patient with yourself and your process.

Reflect here on how mindful eating can change your relationship with food as well as with yourself:

_____

_____

_____

_____

CHAPTER NINE
Movement and Self-Love Throughout Your Lifetime
HEALING YOUR RELATIONSHIP WITH YOUR BODY

"To be beautiful means to be yourself. You don't need to be accepted by others. You need to accept yourself." -Thich Nhat Hanh

So far in this process you have increased your intake of nutrient dense foods, you are drinking more water and clearing out the foods that no longer serve your health goals. Having a healthy relationship with food is essentially having a healthy relationship with yourself. Being able to trust yourself, your choices and at times to get out of your own way (thank you Deal Maker!) are extremely important parts of the process in making peace with food.

Movement and exercise are also particularly important to explore as there is extensive research surrounding the benefits of daily movement or exercise on both mind and body. With research being interesting and certainly important, just doing some type of exercise is enough to *feel* the benefits.

Some of the powerful benefits of exercise include improving mood, reducing the effects of stress mentally and physically, stabilizing blood sugar, improving metabolic functions, increasing strength, decreasing risk of most diseases and illnesses, increasing longevity, and while the list could go on and on you probably see the point. Most importantly exercise can improve self-esteem and confidence, growing your Inner Strength.

The trouble with exercise is that it takes time, it takes consistency, and it takes dedicated focus. Time is often the biggest hindrance for many as life is busy and does not seem to be slowing down anytime soon. Another hindrance can be not liking to exercise. While time is legitimate, most people are overworked and stressed and finding the time can really be a challenge, however, not liking to exercise is an excuse.

Exercising does not have to be running, going to the gym, getting on an elliptical machine or treadmill, unless of course those are your things. You want to find a way of moving your body that is fun, that feels good, and is rewarding.

There are a lot of excuses the Deal Maker can generate to avoid exercise. It is helpful to focus on what you do like about exercising. Focusing on how you feel *after* you exercise can help move past the procrastination and avoidance. You will rarely regret exercising. However, you may regret *not* exercising.

Review the list below. **What do you like to do, or might you enjoy for movement/exercise?**

Dancing?

Swimming?

Water aerobics?

Walking?

Yoga?

Pilates?

Hiking?

Biking?

Playing Tennis?

Taking a group exercise class?

Jogging/running?

Getting on an exercise machine?

Strength training?

Interval training?

Tabata?

Skateboarding?

Rollerskating/rollerblading?

Skiing?

Horseback riding?

Joining a team sports league?

Something else that you like to do? _____

Where would you prefer to do this movement?

At home?

At a gym or studio?

Outside?

With a friend?

Alone?

How many times per week can you commit to doing this movement at this place?

Now that you have a movement you will use and a location and time, how often can you do this? _____

If you are brand new to exercising or just getting back into it, start slowly. Commit to one time per week to begin and increase from there. One time per week is better than none at all. Ten minutes is better than no minutes.

NOW YOU HAVE A *plan,* TIME TO *execute!*

The next exercise will give you the opportunity to log your exercise where you can write down what you do, the duration, how motivated you are to do the exercise before you do it, how you feel following the exercise, and if your motivation was low and what encouraged you to do it anyway.

This feedback will help you focus on how you feel after exercising. This focus is a great motivator to encourage you to be consistent. If you are not feeling motivated, noticing what helped to push you forward on other days will be a tremendous motivator you can use to do it NOW. Keeping your focus on action will help you to continue with your exercise and movement for the long run.

Exercise is important throughout your lifetime. The form that it takes may change at different phases of your life. That is ok. It is doing it that matters. While there are guidelines for how much exercise humans need for increased health benefits, try just to focus on what you can do now. One day is better than zero, ten minutes better than zero. This is not about perfection, it is about finding what works and sticking with it. If it is not working any longer, finding something else and sticking with it.

Log Your Exercise

Use the following chart to log your exercise over the next few weeks being as detailed as possible:

Date/Time/Place	Type of Exercise and Duration	Motivation Level Before Exercising	How Do You Feel Following the Exercise Physically and Energetically?	If Your Motivation Was Low, What Made You DO IT ANYWAY?
Example: Day 1: 9/12/17 6:30am Yoga Studio	Yoga class	Minimal, I really wanted to stay in bed	Physically, I feel stronger and more relaxed, more comfortable in my body. I feel more energized.	I told myself I wanted to be able to log this, I want to become more disciplined with this practice.
Day 1:				
Day 2:				
Day 3:				
Day 4:				
Day 5:				
Day 6:				
Day 7:				

Reflect on your experience after completing the movement/exercise log:

_____

_____

_____

_____

What changes did you notice in your motivation throughout the logging experience?

_____

_____

How did you typically feel following movement/exercise?

_____

_____

What changes did you notice in how you feel about yourself, your body and your relationship with food?

_____

_____

_____

If it has been helpful to log your exercise, continue doing so,

use the tools that work for you.

Body Image AND Self-Esteem

Addressing body image, self-esteem as well as practices that create opportunities to increase your self-love are essential on this path towards making peace with food as well as with yourself.

Delving further into healing your relationship with your body requires thinking kind thoughts about your body. Accepting compliments from others. Saying kind words about your body to yourself or others. Body image is a challenge. It requires acceptance and non-judgment. You may have been taught at a young age that looks are more important than anything. More important than how you feel, how you behave, and the kind of person you are.

Where did it go so wrong? So backwards? Even if you grew up with someone saying to you, *pretty is as pretty does*. Or: *It's what's on the inside that counts*. How much was that reinforced in your life? Probably not much. Our culture celebrates beauty and creates a disturbing image of what it portrays as a "perfect" body.

While it may not be possible to reverse all of the conditioning that goes along with culture such as the images you are bombarded with on TV, in magazines, and on billboards, as well as the judgment that often happens when you are young in social situations. It is possible to create a new perspective on your body as well as on others' bodies. Just like all the other practices, this will take time and effort.

Noticing Body Shame

This is an exercise in paying attention to any *body talk* that you do with others as well as your internal dialogue about your body or others' bodies. This is a practice of being aware of any body shaming you are doing internally, such as mentally commenting about yourself or someone else's body, or externally, making a comment to someone about your or someone else's body, out loud. This is a practice in awareness.

Over the next week spend time noticing comments you make internally or externally regarding your body or someone else's body as well comments others make. List any body talk that you notice here:

Date	Situation and Body Shaming Comments You or Someone Else Made	How You Felt After Noticing the Comment
Example: Day 1: 9/12/17	While looking in the mirror getting dressed, I said to myself: *I hate how I look in these pants*	I felt unattractive and anxious
Day 1:		
Day 2:		

Day 3:		
Day 4:		
Day5:		
Day 6:		
Day 7:		

Reflect on this experience here:

What surprised you about the words you use to describe your own body in your mind?

_____

_____

_____

What surprised you about thoughts you have about other people's bodies?

_____

_____

_____

How often did body talk come up in conversations with others? How often was it positive or negative talk about others?

_____

_____

What surprised you about other people's comments about your body or other people's bodies?

_____

_____

_____

_____

Non-judgmental Awareness of Your Body

Spend some time gazing in the mirror. Label your body parts for what they are without any additional conditions. Just the facts, what is true, without judging your body or this experience. (Example: Your nose is just a nose, used for smelling, breathing, purifying air...)

What was this like for you?

_____

_____

Did any negative judgments come up for you? If so, what were they?

_____

_____

How can you work to let go of those judgements?

_____

_____

What surprised you about this exercise?

_____

_____

Being Kind To Yourself

What is a part of your body that you do like? _____

Spend some time gazing in the mirror and reflecting on the body part you do like.

What was this like for you?

_____

_____

What judgments came up for you?

_____

_____

How can you work to let go of those judgements?

_____

_____

What surprised you about this exercise?

_____

_____

_____

Love Yourself List

Write a list of what you do love about yourself here. They can be both physical and personal attributes, your strengths on the inside as well as outside. (Examples: Physical: My eyes, My hair. Strengths: Patient, Good Listener)

If this is challenging for you, think of how someone who cares about you would describe you. What do they say that they love about you?

1._____

2._____

3._____

4._____

5._____

6._____

7._____

8._____

9._____

10._____

Describe how it feels to reflect on this list:

_____

_____

Practice stating to yourself *out loud* while looking in the mirror one or more of items from your Love Yourself List for a week. Log your experience in the following chart:

Date	Self-Love List Item	How You Feel After
Example: Day 1: 9/12/17	I appreciate my eyes.	It feels awkward to say it out loud. I do feel I can believe it and it feels good.
Day 1:		
Day 2:		
Day 3:		
Day 4:		
Day 5:		
Day 6:		
Day 7:		

Reflect on your experience here:

How did it feel to say something you love about yourself *to yourself* daily?

_____

_____

Was there anything difficult about this practice?

_____

_____

What shifts or changes did you notice?

_____

_____

How did this practice impact your relationship with food?

_____

_____

Will you continue with this practice, why or why not?

_____

_____

Taking Compliments

"The truth is: Belonging starts with self-acceptance. Your level of belonging, in fact, can never be greater than your level of self-acceptance, because believing that you're enough is what gives you the courage to be authentic, vulnerable and imperfect." -Brene Brown

When you receive a compliment how do you typically respond? There is only one way to take a compliment: Say: Thank you. That is all. Zip it!

Practice taking compliments. Notice your tendency to diminish or qualify it. Recognize whatever it is you typically do to it, and stop doing it!

How do you typically diminish or qualify compliments given to you?

_____

_____

After you practice taking a compliment and simply saying Thank You, how did it feel?

_____

_____

_____

Can you commit to this simple practice, why or why not?

_____

_____

_____

Reflect on the exercises throughout this chapter. What impact have movement and exercise as well as the self-image exercises had on how you feel about yourself and your relationship with food?

_____

_____

_____

_____

_____

_____

_____

_____

_____

_____

_____

_____

CHAPTER TEN
Maintaining Your Progress

KEEPING YOUR VISION ALIVE

"Successful people maintain a positive focus in life no matter what is going on around them. They stay focused on their past successes rather than their past failures, and on the next action steps they need to take to get them closer to the fulfillment of their goals rather than all the other distractions that life presents to them." -Jack Canfield

One of the reasons this book does not encourage a specific dietary theory and rather encourages moving away from a dieting mentality is because there is an end point to dieting. There is finality to the goal. This end point might be a weight goal or a clothing size goal. This creates a signal that it is all over, that you are done.

Restriction and dieting often lead to overeating and this creates a negative and damaging cycle. It is like a swinging pendulum. If it swings to the extreme in one direction, it will inevitably swing to the extreme in the other direction. Restriction leads to overeating. Overeating leads to restriction. Moderation, the middle path, is so much more sustainable.

This book instead encouraged you to find and create a pattern of healthy eating, positive self-care, movement and exercise. It encouraged being self-aware and mindful of your emotions, your stress, your food and the impact that they have on your overall health.

Your vision for your life is a lifelong path. There is no endpoint. Progress continues as long as you practice, and as long as you practice you will move forward to where you want to go. Practice establishes consistent effort, always guiding you towards living a life that you love.

Throughout this chapter, you will continue to implement the changes you have made up to this point, while reflecting on how to sustain them throughout your life. There will be setbacks and challenges throughout the process but that is no reason to give up. These setbacks are distractions, and you now have developed the tools to manage and cope effectively with these distractions.

As you move into this reflective mode, complete the following exercise, revisiting the *Circle of Life*: a visual reflection of the balance in your life.

EXERCISE ONE

Circle of Life

Complete the *Circle of Life* exercise. It creates a visual representation of the current balance in your life. Usually when life is out of balance it creates a challenge for food and wellness to be in balance. The exercise considers primary foods to be the elements in your life that nourish you and secondary food to be the food you actually eat. When your primary foods are out of balance it directly impacts your secondary food.

INSTRUCTIONS:

Look at each section and place a dot on the line based on how satisfied you are with each area of your life. A dot placed at the center of the circle would indicate dissatisfaction, while a dot placed closer to the edge indicates complete satisfaction. Once you have placed your dot on each of the lines, connect the dots to see your circle of life. You will have a clear visual representation of any imbalances so you can determine where you could benefit from spending more time and energy to create balance and joy in your life.

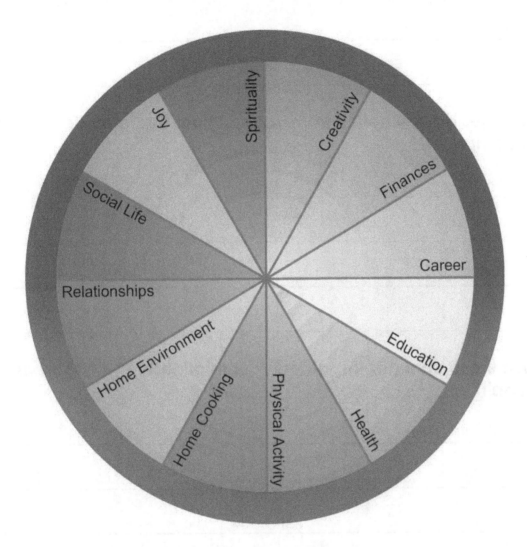

© 2011 Integrative Nutrition Inc.

Reflect on your original *Circle of Life* in comparison to your current *Circle of Life*. **What stands out to you the most?**

_____

_____

_____

What changes do you notice from your original *Circle of Life* to the one you just completed?

_____

_____

_____

How have these changes impacted your relationship with food as well as with yourself?

_____

_____

_____

Are there any elements that surprise you?

_____

_____

_____

Living Your Vision

Take a moment to go back and reread your vision and your goals from chapter 2. **Is there anything you would like to add or change in relation to your vision?**

_____

_____

_____

What goals have you met?

_____

_____

_____

What goals have you struggled with?

_____

_____

_____

What can you do to refocus on your goals?

_____

_____

If you have successfully met your goals, do you have any new goals you would like to set that continue your progress towards your vision? If so take time to set them now.

_____

_____

_____

_____

If you find that you are struggling with a goal, how can you rework it to regain your focus?

_____

_____

_____

_____

Staying IN Action

If you find you are wavering in your actions and the follow-through is just not there, the best place to detect the source of this wavering is your internal belief about yourself. You might have the thought: _I'd like to work on this goal._ However, if your belief about yourself is that you will not follow through, that you will not have time, or that you may not succeed, causing your desire to work on your action steps to not be there. This exercise is about aligning your goals and actions to help maintain motivation.

Aligning What You Want with Your Actions

This journaling exercise is intended to help you keep your own mental wavering in check, and to use action to break through any outpouring fear.

Believing that you are capable of anything you put your mind to can be a difficult concept to fully grasp. The mind may challenge your belief in yourself and your ability to achieve your goals.

Allowing yourself to be open to abundance and achievement is important when moving forward towards your goals and vision. Self-doubt often creeps its way in and must be worked through.

What are some fears and limiting beliefs that stand in your way in relation to your goals, aspirations and vision?

_____

_____

_____

_____

_____

_____

_____

How can you release these fears? What would that take?

_____

_____

_____

_____

What is the cost to you to not let go of the fears?

_____

_____

_____

_____

What action will you take today?

_____

_____

_____

_____

_____

Reflecting on Your Relationship With Food

What changes have you noticed in your relationship with food?

_____

_____

_____

_____

_____

_____

How have these changes impacted your self-esteem?

_____

_____

_____

_____

_____

How have these changes impacted your body-image?

_____

_____

_____

_____

_____

How will you ensure that you will stay on your path towards your vision?

_____

_____

_____

_____

_____

_____

_____

_____

Mandala Reflection

After reflecting on all that you have learned about yourself, create a mandala that reflects how you feel about where you are along your path. Steady your breath, turn your focus inward and reflect on how far you have come. Now use line, shape, color and form to express what came up for you in this reflection with the circle as a guide, not a barrier.

Begin with a color that represents how you feel and begin. Change colors throughout if that suits your process.

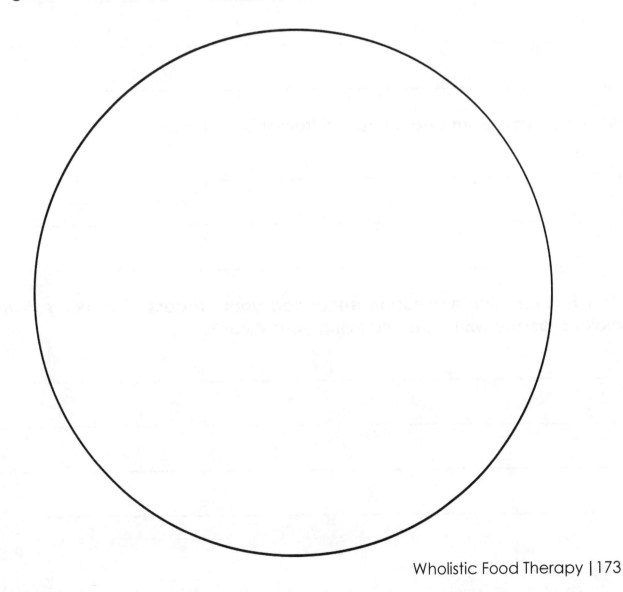

Mandala title: _____

How does your mandala make you feel?

_____

_____

_____

What stands out to you the most?

_____

_____

_____

What can you learn about yourself from this mandala?

_____

_____

_____

How has creative expression enhanced your process of working towards making peace with food and living your vision?

_____

_____

_____

_____

Congratulations!

You have worked really hard through each of these chapters and exercises. Hopefully this work has moved you closer to your vision and closer to living an inspired life. Most likely there is still some work to do, and some areas that are still a challenge.

Believe in yourself and your capacity for growth and change. You will continue to heal your relationship with food as well as with yourself! Continue with the mindfulness practices. This is the basis of staying connected to the present moment. Mindfulness helps to not get caught up in expectations of outcome. It allows you to be with what is true in this moment-the only moment. That is the practice. That is the foundation for growth and change.

Remind yourself to reflect on your goals weekly and monthly. Schedule the time you need to dedicate yourself to this reflection and stick with it. You have the power within you. It is there. Accessing it is up to you. Choose action over fear and you will continue to flourish!

Final Reflection

Create or find an image that represents how you feel about completing this book. Create or attach it here:

MOVING FORWARD ALONG YOUR *Journey*

This book was inspired by my experience at the Institute for Integrative Nutrition® (IIN), where I received my training in holistic wellness and health coaching. IIN offers a truly comprehensive Health Coach Training Program that invites students to deeply explore the things that are most nourishing to them. This is an amazing and well-rounded program that created a major change in my perspective on my own health and wellness.

From the physical aspects of nutrition and eating wholesome foods that work best for each individual person, to the concept of Primary Food – the idea that everything in life, including our spirituality, career, relationships, and fitness contributes to our inner and outer health – IIN helped me reach optimal health and balance. This inner journey unleashed the passion that compels me to share what I've learned and inspire others.

Beyond personal health, IIN offers training in health coaching, as well as business and marketing. Students who choose to pursue this field professionally complete the program equipped with the communication skills and branding knowledge they need to create a fulfilling career encouraging and supporting others in reaching their own health goals. From renowned wellness expert's as Visiting Teachers to the convenience of their online learning platform, this school has changed my life, and I believe it will do the same for you.

I invite you to learn more about the Institute for Integrative Nutrition and explore how the Health Coach Training Program can help you transform your life. Feel free to contact me to hear more about my personal experience at wholisticfoodtherapy@gmail.com, or call IIN directly (844) 315-8546 to learn more.

To share your experience about how this book helped you feel free to contact me! To learn more about working individually with me and up-coming *Wholistic Food Therapy* online courses, visit my website at:

www.wholisticfoodtherapy.com

Email me at
wholisticfoodtherapy@gmail.com

You can follow me on Facebook as well.

I look forward hearing about your path and supporting you along way!

The good life is a process, not a state of being. It is a direction, not a destination.
-Carl Rogers

Special Thanks

Thank you to my amazing husband Phil for your constant support. Throughout this process your patience and belief in me kept me going. I could not have completed this book without you. Thank you to my sister Amy and sister-in-law Sarah for your support and feedback, it gave me confidence to keep going. Thank you to Carrie, and all of my colleagues at Richmond Creative Counseling. I am so grateful to be a part of the practice and for your support. Thank you to all of my friends and family who have supported me throughout this process. Thank you to my brilliant editors, designers and overall book coach support, Amanda, Andrew and your team made it become something I am extremely proud to share!

Resources

Continue to create mandalas, maybe one each week, maybe one each month. There are several here for you to continue exploring your journey through the creative process!

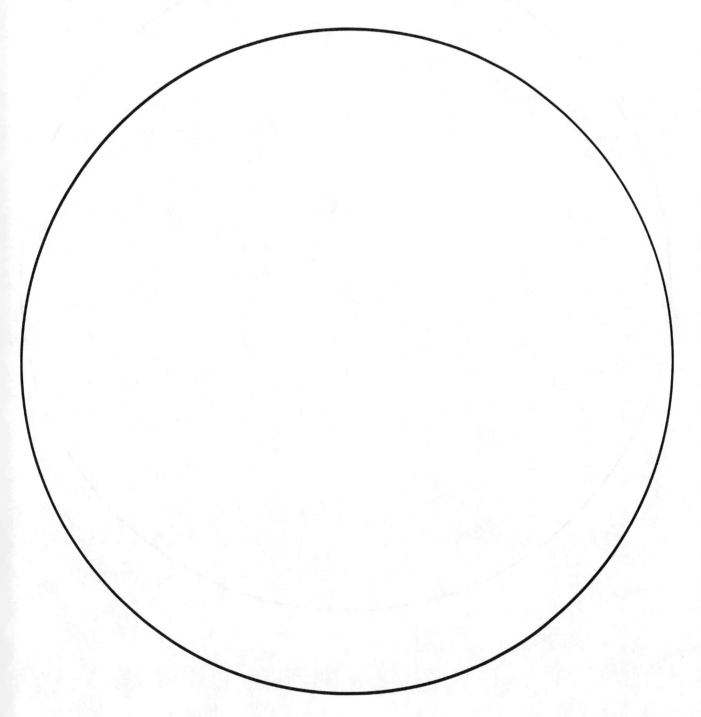

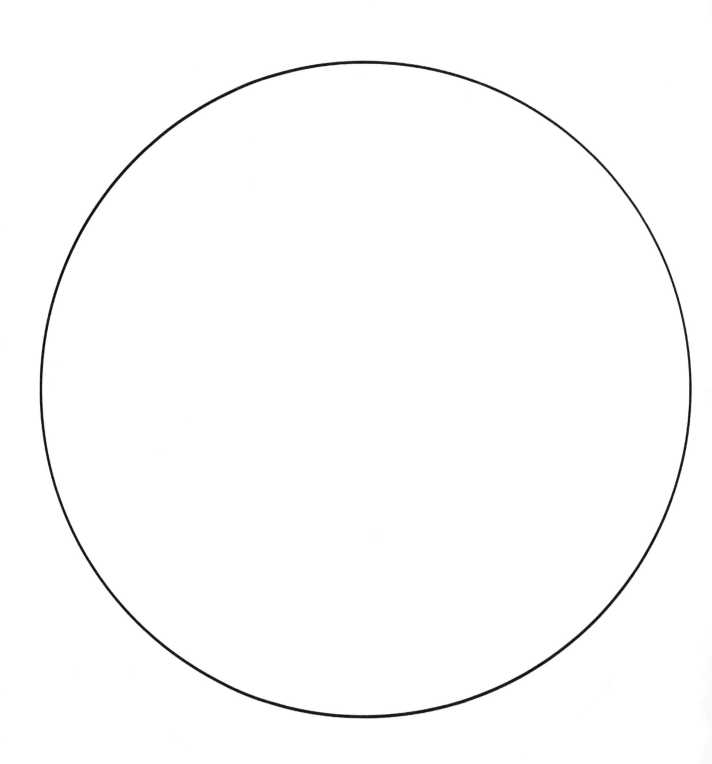

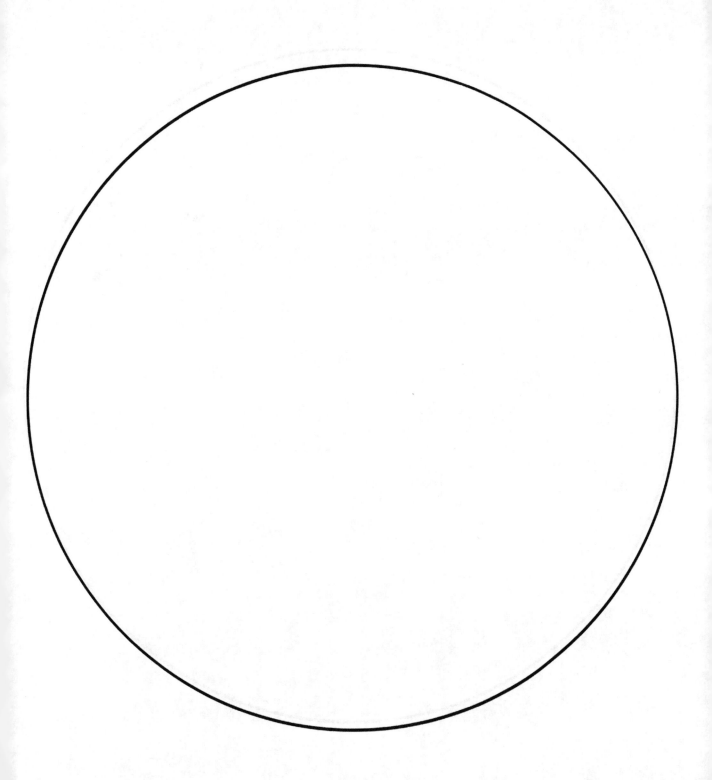

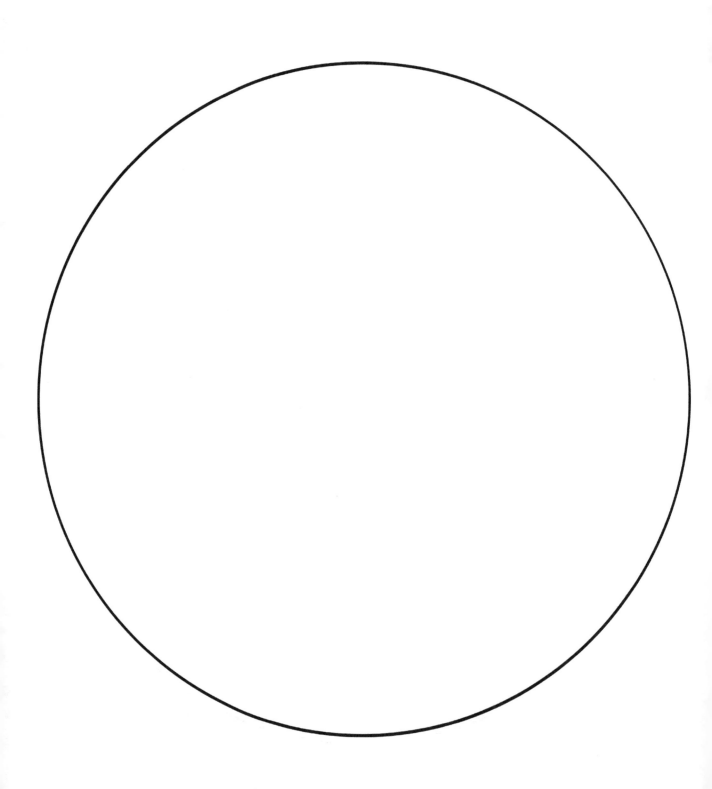

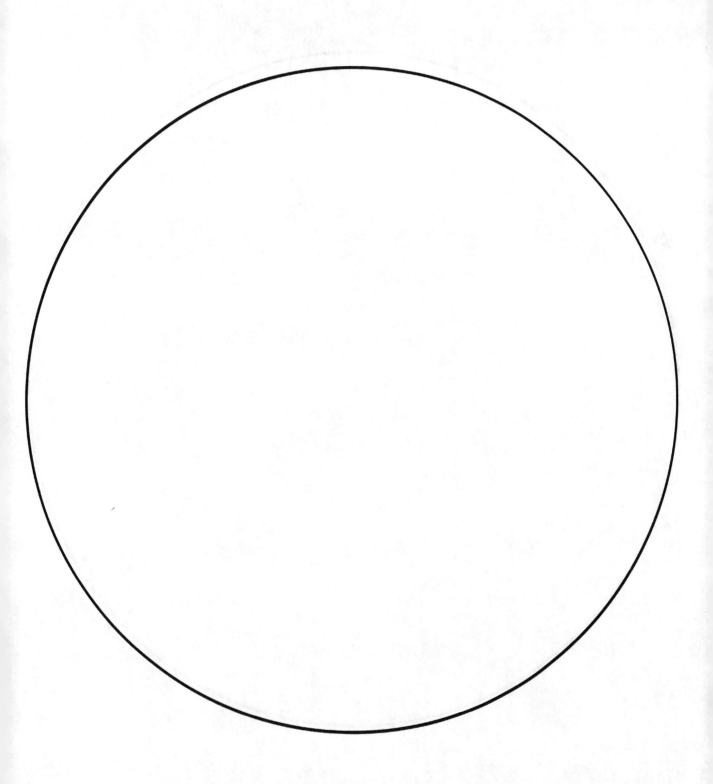

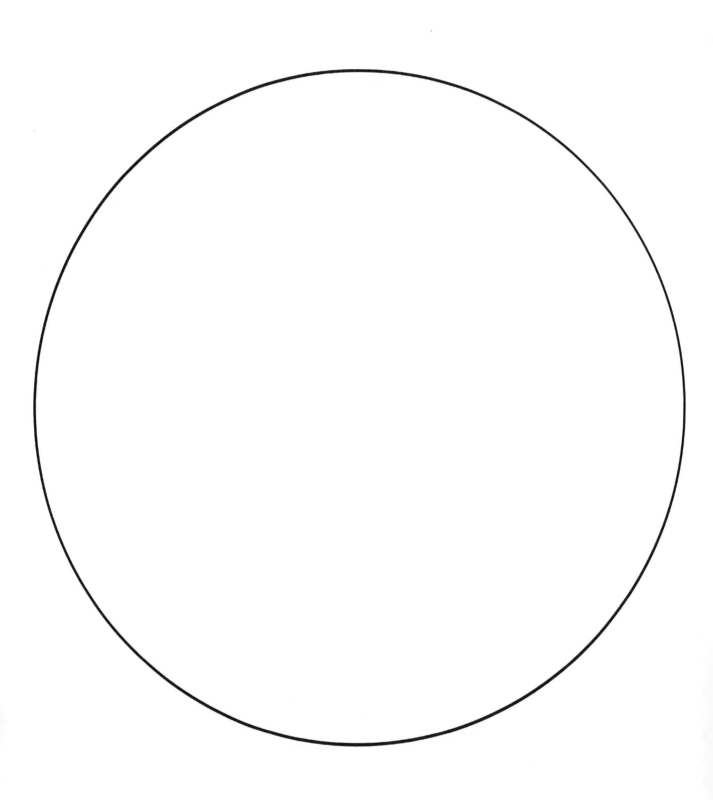

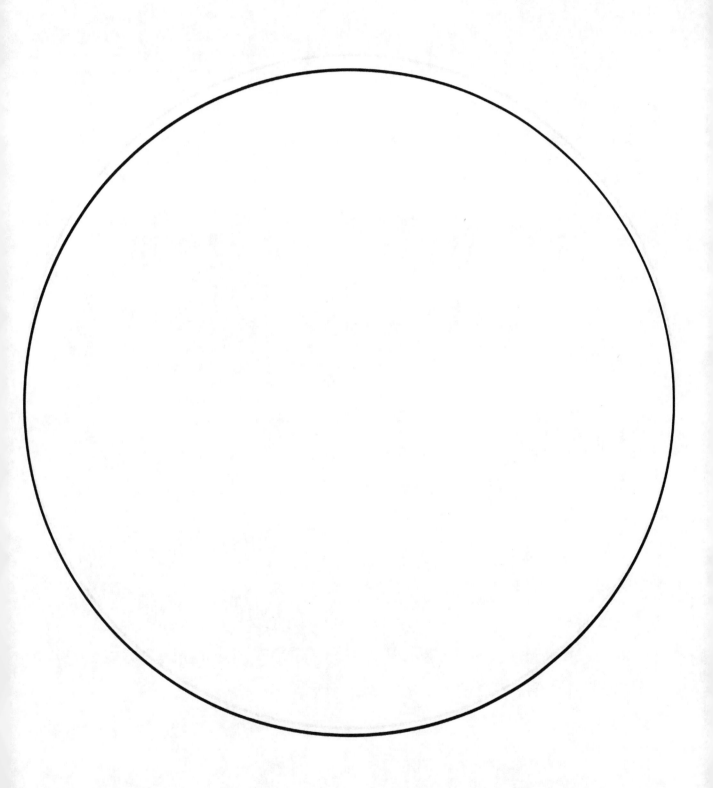

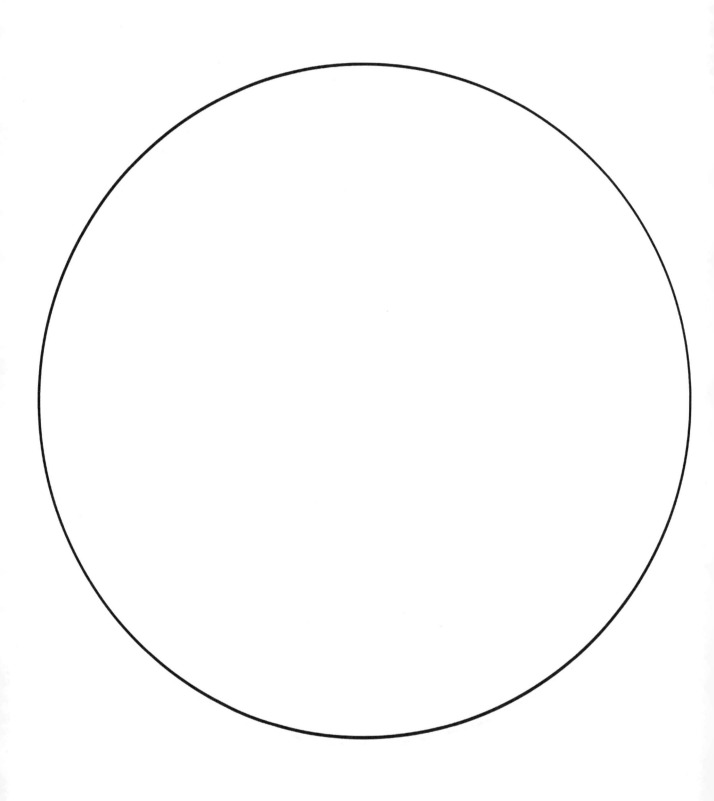

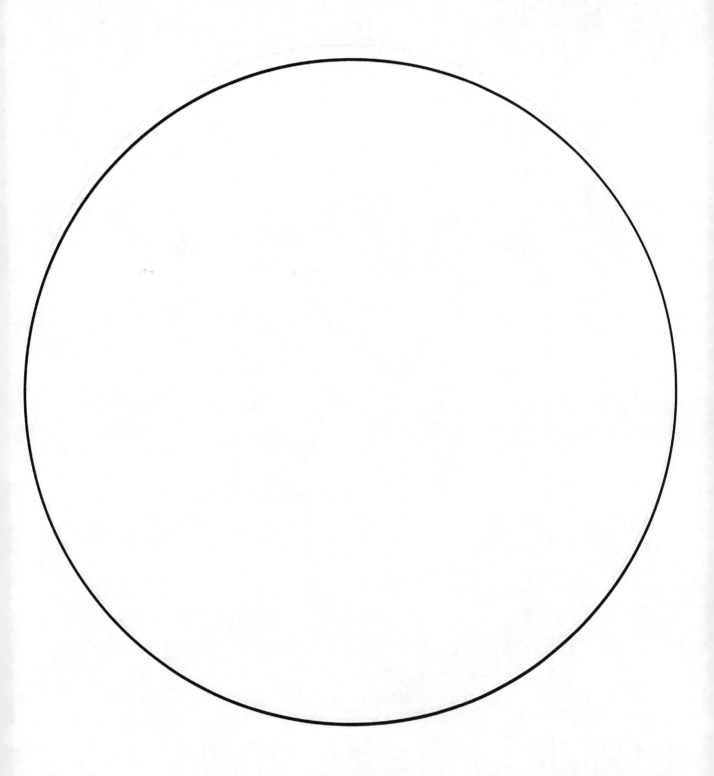

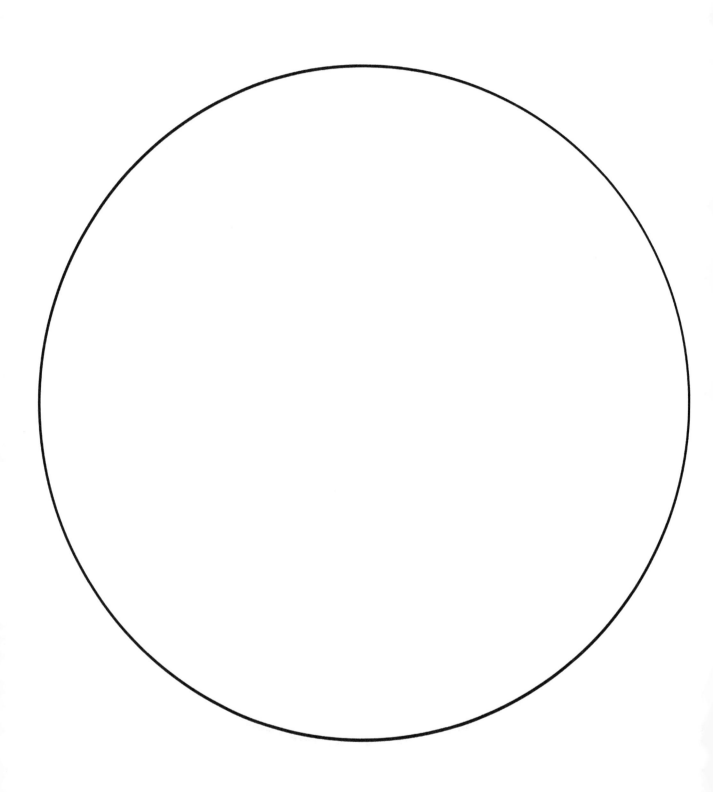

Resources: ADDITIONAL READINGS

Here is a short list of additional readings that can support your process going forward:

Art Therapy:

Malchiodi, J. (2002). The Soul's Palette: Drawing on Arts Transformative Powers

Rappaport, L. (2013). Mindfulness and the Arts Therapies: Theory and Practice

Breathing:

Ballentine, R., Hymes, A., Rama, S. (2007). Science of Breath: A Practical Guide

Farhi, D. (1996). The Breathing Book: Good Health and Vitality Through Essential Breath Work

Food/Nutrition/Health:

Albers, S. (2009). Eat, Drink, and Be Mindful: How to End Your Struggle with Mindless Eating and Start Savoring Food with Intention and Joy

Lipman, F. (2015). The New Health Rules: Simple Changes to Achieve Whole-Body Wellness

Rosenthal, J. (2015) Integrative Nutrition: Feed Your Hunger for Health Happiness

Scott, T. (2011). The Anti-Anxiety Food Solution: How the Foods You Eat Can Help You Calm Your Anxious Mind, Improve Your Mood & End Cravings

Mindfulness:

Tolle, E. (2004). The Power of Now: A Guide to Spiritual Enlightenment

Hanh, T. (2010). You Are Here: Discovering the Magic of the Present Moment

Hanh, T. (2012). Peace is Every Breath

Kabat-Zinn, J. (2013). Full Catastrophe Living (revised edition): Using the Wisdom of Your Body and Mind to Face Stress, Pain and Illness

Mindset:

Dweck, C. (2007). Mindset: The New Psychology of Success

Visioning:

Beckwith, M. (2013). Life Visioning: A Transformative Process for Activating Your Unique Gifts and Highest Potential